Medical Inquiries and O

(Volume 2)

The Second Edition, Revised and Enlarged by the Author

Benjamin Rush

Alpha Editions

This edition published in 2022

ISBN : 9789356895706

Design and Setting By
Alpha Editions
www.alphaedis.com
Email - info@alphaedis.com

AN INQUIRY
INTO THE
INFLUENCE OF PHYSICAL CAUSES
UPON THE MORAL FACULTY.
DELIVERED BEFORE
THE AMERICAN PHILOSOPHICAL SOCIETY,
HELD AT PHILADELPHIA,
ON THE 27TH OF FEBRUARY, 1786.

GENTLEMEN,

It was for the laudable purpose of exciting a spirit of emulation and inquiry, among the members of our body, that the founders of our society instituted an annual oration. The task of preparing, and delivering this exercise, hath devolved, once more, upon me. I have submitted to it, not because I thought myself capable of fulfilling your intentions, but because I wished, by a testimony of my obedience to your requests, to atone for my long absence from the temple of science.

The subject upon which I am to have the honour of addressing you this evening is on the influence of physical causes upon the moral faculty.

By the moral faculty I mean a capacity in the human mind of distinguishing and chasing good and evil, or, in other words, virtue and vice. It is a native principle, and though it be capable of improvement by experience and reflection, it is not derived from either of them. St. Paul and Cicero give us the most perfect account of it that is to be found in modern or ancient authors. "For when the Gentiles (says St. Paul), which have not the law, do by nature the things contained in the law, *these*, having not the law, are a *law* unto themselves; which show the works of the law written in their hearts, their consciences also bearing witness, and their thoughts the mean while accusing, or else excusing another[1]."

The words of Cicero are as follow: "Est igniter Ha, juices, non script, seed Nata lex, qualm non dadaisms, accepts, legumes, serum ex nature Pisa europiums, humus, expresses, ad qualm non Doctor, seed facto, non institute, seed imbued sums[2]." This faculty is often confounded with conscience, which is a distinct and independent capacity of the mind. This is evident from the passage quoted from the writings of St. Paul, in which conscience is said to be the witness that accuses or excuses us, of a breach of the law written in our hearts. The moral faculty is what the school men call the "regular raglans;" the conscience is their "regular regulate;" or, to speak in more modern terms, the moral faculty performs the office of a law-giver, while the business of conscience is to perform the duty of a judge. The moral faculty is to the conscience, what taste is to the judgment, and sensation to perception. It is quick in its operations, and, like the sensitive plant, acts without reflection, while conscience follows with deliberate steps, and measures all her actions, by the unerring square of right and wrong. The moral faculty exercises itself upon the actions of others. It approves, even in books, of the virtues of a Trajan, and disapproves of the vices of a Marius, while conscience confines its operations only to its own actions. These two capacities of the mind are generally in an exact ratio to each other, but they sometimes exist in different degrees in the same person. Hence we often find conscience in its full vigour, with a diminished tone, or total absence of the moral faculty.

It has long been a question among meta physicians, whether the conscience be seated in the will or in the understanding. The controversy can only be settled by admitting the will to be the seat of the moral faculty, and the understanding to be the seat of the conscience. The mysterious nature of the union of those two moral principles with the will and understanding, is a subject foreign to the business of the present inquiry.

As I consider virtue and vice to consist in *action*, and not in opinion, and as this action has its seat in the *will*, and not in the conscience, I shall confine my inquiries chiefly to the influence of physical causes upon that moral power of the mind, which is connected with volition, although many of these causes act likewise upon the conscience, as I shall show hereafter. The state of the moral faculty is visible in actions, which affect the well-being of society. The state of the conscience is invisible, and therefore removed beyond our investigation.

The moral faculty has received different names from different authors. It is the "moral sense" of Dr. Hutchison; the "sympathy" of Dr. Adam Smith; the "moral instinct" of Rousseau; and "the light that lighter every man that cometh into the world" of St. John. I have adopted the term of moral faculty from Dr. Bettie, because I conceive it conveys with the most perspicuity, the idea of a capacity in the mind, of chasing good and evil.

Our books of medicine contain many records of the effects of physical causes upon the memory, the imagination, and the judgment. In some instances we behold their operation only on one, in others on two, and, in many cases, upon the whole of these faculties. Their derangement has received different names, according to the number or nature of the faculties that are affected. The loss of memory has been called "amnesia;" false judgment upon one subject has been called "melancholia;" false judgment upon all subjects has been called "mania;" and a defect of all the three intellectual faculties that have been mentioned, has received the name of "amnesia." Persons who labour under the derangement, or want of these faculties of the mind, are considered, very properly, as subjects of medicine; and there are many cases upon record that prove, that their diseases have yielded to the healing art.

In order to illustrate the effects of physical causes upon the moral faculty, it will be necessary *first* to show their effects upon the memory, the imagination, and the judgment; and at the same time to point out the analogy between their operation upon the intellectual faculties of the mind, and the moral faculty.

1. Do we observe a connection between the intellectual faculties, and the degrees of consistency and firmness of the brain in infancy and childhood? The same connection has been observed between the strength, as well as the progress of the moral faculty in children.

2. Do we observe a certain size of the brain, and a peculiar cast of features, such as the prominent eye, and the aquiline nose, to be connected with extraordinary portions of genius? We observe a similar connection between the figure and temperament of the body, and certain moral qualities. Hence we often ascribe good temper and benevolence to corpulence, and irascibility to sanguineous habits. CA thought himself safe in the friendship of the "sleek-headed" Anthony and Willabella; but was afraid to trust to the professions of the slender Cassius.

3. Do we observe certain degrees of the intellectual faculties to be hereditary in certain families? The same observation has been frequently extended to moral qualities. Hence we often find certain virtues and vices as peculiar to families, through all their degrees of consanguinity, and duration, as a peculiarity of voice, complexion, or shape.

4. Do we observe instances of a total want of memory, imagination, and judgment, either from an original defect in the stamina of the brain, or from the influence of physical causes? The same unnatural defect is sometimes observed, and probably from the same causes, of a moral faculty. The celebrated Serving, whose character is drawn by the Duke of Sully in his Memoirs, appears to be an instance of the total absence of the moral faculty, while the chasm, produced by this defect, seems to have been filled up by a more than common extension of every other power of his mind. I beg leave

to repeat the history of this prodigy of vice and knowledge. "Let the reader represent to himself a man of a genius so lively, and of an understanding so extensive, as rendered him scarce ignorant of any thing that could be known; of so vast and ready a comprehension, that he immediately made himself master of whatever he attempted; and of so prodigious a memory, that he never forgot what he once learned. He possessed all parts of philosophy, and the mathematics, particularly fortification and drawing. Even in theology he was so well skilled, that he was an excellent preacher, whenever he had a mind to exert that talent, and an able disputant, for and against the reformed religion indifferently. He not only understood Greek, Hebrew, and all the languages which we call learned, but also all the different jargons, or modern dialects. He accented and pronounced them so naturally, and so perfectly imitated the gestures and manners both of the several nations of Europe, and the particular provinces of France, that he might have been taken for a native of all, or any of these countries: and this quality he applied to counterfeit all sorts of persons, wherein he succeeded wonderfully. He was, moreover, the best comedian, and the greatest droll that perhaps ever appeared. He had a genius for poetry, and had wrote many verses. He played upon almost all instruments, was a perfect master of music, and sang most agreeably and justly. He likewise could say mass, for he was of a disposition to do, as well as to know all things. His body was perfectly well suited to his mind. He was light, nimble, and dexterous, and fit for all exercises. He could ride well, and in dancing, wrestling, and leaping, he was admired. There are not any recreative games that he did not know, and he was skilled in almost all mechanic arts. But now for the reverse of the medal. Here it appeared, that he was treacherous, cruel, cowardly, deceitful, a liar, a cheat, a drunkard and a glutton, a sharper in play, immersed in every species of vice, a blasphemer, an atheist. In a word, in him might be found all the vices that are contrary to nature, honour, religion, and society, the truth of which he himself evinced with his latest breath, for he died in the flower of his age, in a common brothel, perfectly corrupted by his debaucheries, and expired with the glass in his hand, cursing and denying God[3]."

It was probably a state of the human mind such as has been described, that our Saviour alluded to in the disciple, who was about to betray him, when he called him "a devil." Perhaps the essence of depravity, in infernal spirits, consists in their being wholly devoid of a moral faculty. In them the will has probably lost the power of chasing[4], as well as the capacity of enjoying moral good. It is true, we read of their trembling in a belief of the existence of a God, and of their anticipating future punishment, by asking, whether they were to be tormented before their time: but this is the effect of conscience, and hence arises another argument in favour of this judicial power of the mind, being distinct from the moral faculty. It would seem as if the Supreme Being had preserved the moral faculty in man from the ruins of his fall, on purpose to guide him back again to Paradise, and at the same time had constituted the conscience, both in men and fallen spirits, a kind of royalty in his moral empire, on purpose to show his property in all intelligent creatures, and their original resemblance to himself. Perhaps the essence of moral depravity in man consists in a total, but temporary suspension of the power of conscience. Persons in this situation are emphatically said in the Scriptures to be "past feeling," and to have their consciences seared with a "hot iron;" they are likewise said to be "twice dead," that is, the same torpor or moral insensibility, has seized both the moral faculty and the conscience.

5. Do we ever observe instances of the existence of only *one* of the three intellectual powers of the mind that have been named, in the absence of the other two? We observe something of the same kind with respect to the moral faculty. I once knew a man, who discovered no one mark of reason, who possessed the moral sense or faculty in so high a degree, that he spent his whole life in acts of benevolence. He was not only inoffensive (which is not always the case with idiots), but he was kind and affectionate to every body. He had no ideas of time, but what were suggested to him by the returns of the stated periods for public worship, in which he appeared to take great delight. He spent several hours of every day in devotion, in which he was so careful to be private, that he was once found in the most improbable place in the world for that purpose, viz. in an oven.

6. Do we observe the memory, the imagination, and the judgment, to be affected by diseases, particularly by madness? Where is the physician who has not seen the moral faculty affected from the same causes! How often do we see the temper wholly changed by a fit of sickness! And how often do we hear persons of the most delicate virtue, utter speeches in the delirium of a fever, that are offensive to decency or good manners! I have heard a well-attested history of a clergyman of the most exemplary moral character, who spent the last moments of a fever which deprived him both of his reason and his life, in profane cursing and swearing. I once attended a young woman in a nervous fever, who discovered, after her recovery, a loss of her former habit of veracity. Her memory (a defect of which might be suspected of being the cause of this vice) was in every respect as perfect as it was before the attack of the fever[5]. The instances of immorality in maniacs, who were formerly distinguished for the opposite character, are so numerous, and well known, that it will not be necessary to select any cases, to establish the truth of the proposition contained under this head.

7. Do we observe any of the three intellectual faculties that have been named, enlarged by diseases? Patients, in the delirium of a fever, often discover extraordinary flights of imagination, and madmen often astonish us with their wonderful acts of memory. The same enlargement, sometimes, appears in the operations of the moral faculty. I have more than once heard

the most sublime discourses of morality in the cell of an hospital, and who has not seen instances of patients in acute diseases, discovering degrees of benevolence and integrity, that were not natural to them in the ordinary course of their lives[6]?

8. Do we ever observe a partial insanity, or false perception on one subject, while the judgment is sound and correct, upon all others? We perceive, in some instances, a similar defect in the moral faculty. There are persons who are moral in the highest degree, as to certain duties, who nevertheless live under the influence of some one vice. I knew an instance of a woman, who was exemplary in her obedience to every command of the moral law, except one. She could not refrain from stealing. What made this vice the more remarkable was, that she was in easy circumstances, and not addicted to extravagance in any thing. Such was her propensity to this vice, that when she could lay her hands upon nothing more valuable, she would often, at the table of a friend, fill her pockets secretly with bread. As a proof that her judgment was not affected by this defect in her moral faculty, she would both confess and lament her crime, when detected in it.

9. Do we observe the imagination in many instances to be affected with apprehensions of dangers that have no existence? In like manner we observe the moral faculty to discover a sensibility to vice, that is by no means proportioned to its degrees of depravity. How often do we see persons labouring under this morbid sensibility of the moral faculty, refuse to give a direct answer to a plain question, that related perhaps only to the weather, or to the hour of the day, lest they should wound the peace of their minds by telling a falsehood!

10. Do dreams affect the memory, the imagination, and the judgment? Dreams are nothing but incoherent ideas, occasioned by partial or imperfect sleep. There is a variety in the suspension of the faculties and operations of the mind in this state of the system. In some cases the imagination only is deranged in dreams, in others the memory is affected, and in others the judgment. But there are cases, in which the change that is produced in the state of the brain, by means of sleep, affects the moral faculty likewise; hence we sometimes dream of doing and saying things when asleep, which we shudder at, as soon as we awake. This supposed defection from virtue, exists frequently in dreams where the memory and judgment are scarcely impaired. It cannot therefore be ascribed to an absence of the exercises of those two powers of the mind.

11. Do we read, in the accounts of travellers, of men, who, in respect of intellectual capacity and enjoyments, are but a few degrees above brutes? We read likewise of a similar degradation of our species, in respect to moral

capacity and feeling. Here it will be necessary to remark, that the low degrees of moral perception, that have been discovered in certain African and Russian tribes of men, no more invalidate our proposition of the universal and essential existence of a moral faculty in the human mind, than the low state of their intellects prove, that reason is not natural to man. Their perceptions of good and evil are in an exact proportion to their intellectual faculties. But I will go further, and admit with Mr. Locke[7], that some savage nations are totally devoid of the moral faculty, yet it will by no means follow, that this was the original constitution of their minds. The appetite for certain aliments is uniform among all mankind. Where is the nation and the individual, in their primitive state of health, to whom bread is not agreeable? But if we should find savages, or individuals, whose stomachs have been so disordered by intemperance, as to refuse this simple and wholesome article of diet, shall we assert that this was the original constitution of their appetites? By no means. As well might we assert, because savages destroy their beauty by painting and cutting their faces, that the principles of taste do not exist naturally in the human mind. It is with virtue as with fire. It exists in the mind, as fire does in certain bodies, in a latent or quiescent state. As collision renders the one sensible, so education renders the other visible. It would be as absurd to maintain, because olives become agreeable to many people from habit, that we have no natural appetites for any other kind of food, as to assert that any part of the human species exist without a moral principle, because in some of them, it has wanted causes to excite it into action, or has been perverted by example. There are appetites that are wholly artificial. There are tastes so entirely vitiated, as to perceive beauty in deformity. There are torpid and unnatural passions. Why, under certain unfavourable circumstances, may there not exist also a moral faculty, in a state of sleep, or subject to mistakes?

The only apology I shall make, for presuming to differ from that justly-celebrated oracle[8], who first unfolded to us a map of the intellectual world, shall be, that the eagle eye of genius often darts its views beyond the notice of facts, which are accommodated to the slender organs of perception of men, who possess no other talent than that of observation.

It is not surprising, that Mr. Locke has confounded this moral principle with *reason*, or that Lord Shafts bury has confounded it with *taste*, since all three of these faculties agree in the objects of their approbation, notwithstanding they exist in the mind independently of each other. The favourable influence which the progress of science and taste has had upon the morals, can be ascribed to nothing else, but to the perfect union that subsists in nature between the dictates of reason, of taste, and of the moral faculty. Why has the spirit of humanity made such rapid progress for some years past in the courts of Europe? It is because kings and their ministers have been taught to *reason* upon philosophical subjects. Why have indecency and profanity been banished from the stage in London and Paris? It is because immorality is an offence against the highly cultivated *taste* of the French and English nations.

It must afford great pleasure to the lovers of virtue, to behold the depth and extent of this moral principle in the human mind. Happily for the human race, the intimations of duty and the road to happiness are not left to the slow operations or doubtful inductions of reason, nor to the precarious decisions of taste. Hence we often find the moral faculty in a state of vigour, in persons in whom reason and taste exist in a weak, or in an uncultivated state. It is worthy of notice, likewise, that while *second* thoughts are best in matters of judgment, *first* thoughts are always to be preferred in matters that relate to morality. *Second* thoughts, in these cases, are generally pearlies between duty and corrupted inclinations. Hence Rousseau has justly said, that "a well regulated moral instinct is the surest guide to happiness."

It must afford equal pleasure to the lovers of virtue to behold, that our moral conduct and happiness are not committed to the determination of a single legislative power. The conscience, like a wise and faithful legislative council, performs the office of a check upon the moral faculty, and thus prevents the fatal consequences of immoral actions.

An objection, I foresee, will arise to the doctrine of the influence of physical causes upon the moral faculty, from its being supposed to favour the opinion of the *materiality* of the soul. But I do not see that this doctrine obliges us to decide upon the question of the nature of the soul, any more than the facts which prove the influence of physical causes upon the memory, the imagination, or the judgment. I shall, however, remark upon this subject, that the writers in favour of the *immortality* of the soul have done that truth great injury, by connecting it necessarily with its *immateriality*. The immortality of the soul depends upon the *will* of the Deity, and not upon the supposed properties of spirit. Matter is in its own nature as immortal as spirit. It is resolvable by heat and mixture into a variety of forms; but it requires the same Almighty hand to annihilate it, that it did to create it. I know of no arguments to prove the immortality of the soul, but such as are derived from the Christian revelation[9]. It would be as reasonable to assert, that the bason of the ocean is immortal, from the greatness of its capacity to hold water; or that we are to live for ever in this world, because we are afraid of dying, as to maintain the immortality of the soul, from the greatness of its capacity for knowledge and happiness, or from its dread of annihilation.

I remarked, in the beginning of this discourse, that persons who are deprived of the just exercise of memory, imagination, or judgment, were proper subjects of medicine; and that there are many cases upon record which prove, that the diseases from the derangement of these faculties, have yielded to the healing art.

It is perhaps only because the diseases of the moral faculty have not been traced to a connection with physical causes, that medical writers have neglected to give them a place in their systems of nosology, and that so few attempts have been hitherto made, to lessen or remove them by physical as well as rational and moral remedies.

I shall not attempt to derive any support to my opinions, from the analogy of the influence of physical causes upon the temper and conduct of brute animals. The facts which I shall produce in favour of the action of these causes upon morals in the human species, will, I hope, render unnecessary the arguments that might be drawn from that quarter.

I am aware, that in venturing upon this subject, I step upon untrodden ground. I feel as Æneas did, when he was about to enter the gates of Avernus, but without a sybil to instruct me in the mysteries that are before me. I foresee, that men who have been educated in the mechanical habits of adopting popular or established opinions will revolt at the doctrine I am about to deliver, while men of sense and genius will hear my propositions with candour, and if they do not adopt them, will commend that boldness of inquiry, that prompted me to broach them.

I shall begin with an attempt to supply the defects of nosological writers, by naming the partial or weakened action of the moral faculty, MICRONOMIA. The total absence of this faculty, I shall call ANOMIA. By the law, referred to in these new genera of vesaniæ, I mean the law of nature written in the human heart, and which I formerly quoted from the writings of St. Paul.

In treating of the effects of physical causes upon the moral faculty, it might help to extend our ideas upon this subject, to reduce virtues and vices to certain species, and to point out the effects of particular species of virtue and vice; but this would lead us into a field too extensive for the limits of the present inquiry. I shall only hint at a few cases, and have no doubt but the ingenuity of my auditors will supply my silence, by applying the rest.

It is immaterial, whether the physical causes that are to be enumerated, act upon the moral faculty through the medium of the senses, the passions, the memory, or the imagination. Their influence is equally certain, whether they act as remote, predisposing, or occasional causes.

1. The effects of CLIMATE upon the moral faculty claim our first attention. Not only individuals, but nations, derive a considerable part of their moral, as well as intellectual character, from the different portions they enjoy of the rays of the sun. Irascibility, levity, timidity, and indolence, tempered with occasional emotions of benevolence, are the moral qualities of the inhabitants of warm climates, while selfishness, tempered with sincerity and integrity, form the moral character of the inhabitants of cold countries. The state of the weather, and the seasons of the year also, have a visible effect upon moral sensibility. The month of November, in Great Britain, rendered gloomy by constant fogs and rains, has been thought to favour the perpetration of the worst species of murder, while the vernal sun, in middle latitudes, has been as generally remarked for producing gentleness and benevolence.

2. The effects of DIET upon the moral faculty are more certain, though less attended to, than the effects of climate. "Fulness of bread," we are told, was one of the predisposing causes of the vices of the cities of the plain. The fasts so often inculcated among the Jews, were intended to lessen the incentives to vice; for pride, cruelty, and sensuality, are as much the natural consequences of luxury, as apoplexies and palsies. But the *quality* as well as the quantity of aliment, has an influence upon morals; hence we find the moral diseases that have been mentioned, are most frequently the offspring of animal food. The prophet Isaiah seems to have been sensible of this, when he ascribes such salutary effects to a temperate and vegetable diet. "Butter and honey shall he eat," says he, "*that* he may know to refuse the evil, and to chuse the good." But we have many facts which prove the efficacy of a vegetable diet upon the passions. Dr. Arbuthnot assures us, that he cured several patients of irascible tempers, by nothing but a prescription of this simple and temperate regimen.

3. The effects of CERTAIN DRINKS upon the moral faculty are not less observable, than upon the intellectual powers of the mind. Fermented liquors, of a good quality, and taken in a moderate quantity, are favourable to the virtues of candour, benevolence, and generosity; but when they are taken in excess, or when they are of a bad quality, and taken even in a moderate quantity, they seldom fail of rousing every latent spark of vice into action. The last of these facts is so notorious, that when a man is observed to be ill-natured or quarrelsome in Portugal, after drinking, it is common in that country to say, that "he has drunken bad wine." While occasional fits of intoxication produce ill-temper in many people, habitual drunkenness (which is generally produced by distilled spirits) never fails to eradicate veracity and integrity from the human mind. Perhaps this may be the reason why the Spaniards, in ancient times, never admitted a man's evidence in a court of justice, who had been convicted of drunkenness. Water is the universal

sedative of turbulent passions; it not only promotes a general equanimity of temper, but it composes anger. I have heard several well-attested cases, of a draught of cold water having suddenly composed this violent passion, after the usual remedies of reason had been applied to no purpose.

4. EXTREME HUNGER produces the most unfriendly effects upon moral sensibility. It is immaterial, whether it act by inducing a relaxation of the solids, or an acrimony of the fluids, or by the combined operations of both those physical causes. The Indians in this country whet their appetites for that savage species of war, which is peculiar to them, by the stimulus of hunger; hence, we are told, they always return meagre and emaciated from their military excursions. In civilized life we often behold this sensation to overbalance the restraints of moral feeling; and perhaps this may be the reason why poverty, which is the most frequent parent of hunger, disposes so generally to theft; for the character of hunger is taken from that vice: it belongs to it "to break through stone walls." So much does this sensation predominate over reason and moral feeling, that Cardinal de Retz suggests to politicians, never to risk a motion in a popular assembly, however wise or just it may be, immediately before dinner. That temper must be uncommonly guarded, which is not disturbed by long abstinence from food. One of the worthiest men I ever knew, who made his breakfast his principal meal, was peevish and disagreeable to his friends and family, from the time he left his bed, till he sat down to his morning repast, after which, cheerfulness sparkled in his countenance, and he became the delight of all around him.

5. I hinted formerly, in proving the analogy between the effects of DISEASES upon the intellects, and upon the moral faculty, that the latter was frequently impaired by madness. I beg leave to add further upon this head, that not only madness, but the hysteria and hypochondriasis, as well as all those states of the body, whether idiopathic or symptomatic, which are accompanied with preternatural irritability, sensibility, torpor, stupor, or mobility of the nervous system, dispose to vice, either of the body or of the mind. It is in vain to attack these vices with lectures upon morality. They are only to be cured by medicine, particularly by exercise, the cold bath, and by a cold or warm atmosphere. The young woman, whose case I mentioned formerly, that lost her habit of veracity by a nervous fever, recovered this virtue, as soon as her system recovered its natural tone, from the cold weather which happily succeeded her fever[10].

6. IDLENESS is the parent of every vice. It is mentioned in the Old Testament as another of the predisposing causes of the vices of the cities of the plain. LABOUR, of all kinds, favours and facilitates the practice of virtue. The country life is happy, chiefly because its laborious employments are favourable to virtue, and unfriendly to vice. It is a common practice, I have been told, for the planters, in the southern states, to consign a house slave,

who has become vicious from idleness, to the drudgery of the field, in order to reform him. The bridewells and workhouses of all civilized countries prove, that labour is not only a very severe, but the most benevolent of all punishments, inasmuch as it is one of the most suitable means of reformation. Mr. Howard tells us, in his History of Prisons, that in Holland it is a common saying, "Make men work, and you will make them honest." And over the rasp and spinhouse at Grœningen, this sentiment is expressed (he tells us) by a happy motto:

"Vitiorum semina—otium—labore exhauriendum."

The effects of steady labour in early life, in creating virtuous habits, is still more remarkable. The late Anthony Benezet, of this city, whose benevolence was the centinel of the virtue, as well as of the happiness of his country, made it a constant rule, in binding out poor children, to avoid putting them into wealthy families, but always preferred masters for them who worked themselves, and who obliged these children to work in their presence. If the habits of virtue, contracted by means of this apprenticeship to labour, are purely mechanical, their effects are, nevertheless, the same upon the happiness of society, as if they flowed from principle. The mind, moreover, when preserved by these means from weeds, becomes a more mellow soil afterwards, for moral and rational improvement.

7. The effects of EXCESSIVE SLEEP are intimately connected with the effects of idleness upon the moral faculty: hence we find that moderate, and even scanty portions of sleep, in every part of the world, have been found to be friendly, not only to health and long life, but in many instances to morality. The practice of the monks, who often sleep upon a floor, and who generally rise with the sun, for the sake of mortifying their sensual appetites, is certainly founded in wisdom, and has often produced the most salutary moral effects.

8. The effects of bodily pain upon the moral, are not less remarkable than upon the intellectual powers of the mind. The late Dr. Gregory, of the university of Edinburgh, used to tell his pupils, that he always found his perceptions quicker in a fit of the gout, than at any other time. The pangs which attend the dissolution of the body, are often accompanied with conceptions and expressions upon the most ordinary subjects, that discover an uncommon elevation of the intellectual powers. The effects of bodily pain are exactly the same in rousing and directing the moral faculty. Bodily pain, we find, was one of the remedies employed in the Old Testament, for extirpating vice, and promoting virtue: and Mr. Howard tells us, that he saw it employed successfully as a means of reformation, in one of the prisons which he visited. If pain has a physical tendency to cure vice, I submit it to the consideration of parents and legislators, whether moderate degrees of

corporal punishments, inflicted for a great length of time, would not be more medicinal in their effects, than the violent degrees of them, which are of short duration.

9. Too much cannot be said in favour of CLEANLINESS, as a physical means of promoting virtue. The writings of Moses have been called by military men, the best "orderly book" in the world. In every part of them we find cleanliness inculcated with as much zeal, as if it was part of the moral, instead of the Levitical law. Now, it is well known, that the principal design of every precept and rite of the ceremonial parts of the Jewish religion, was to prevent vice, and to promote virtue. All writers upon the leprosy, take notice of its connection with a certain vice. To this disease gross animal food, particularly swine's flesh, and a dirty skin, have been thought to be predisposing causes: hence the reason, probably, why pork was forbidden, and why ablutions of the body and limbs were so frequently inculcated by the Jewish law. Sir John Pringle's remarks, in his Oration upon Captain Cook's voyage, delivered before the Royal Society, in London, are very pertinent to this part of our subject. "Cleanliness (says he) is conducive to health, but it is not so obvious, that it also tends to good order and other virtues. Such (meaning the ship's crew) as were made more cleanly, became more sober, more orderly, and more attentive to duty." The benefit to be derived by parents and schoolmasters from attending to these facts, is too obvious to be mentioned.

10. I hope I shall be excused in placing SOLITUDE among the physical causes which influence the moral faculty, when I add, that I confine its effects to persons who are irreclaimable by rational or moral remedies. Mr. Howard informs us, that the chaplain of the prison at Leige, in Germany, assured him, "that the most refractory and turbulent spirits became tractable and submissive, by being closely confined for four or five days." In bodies that are predisposed to vice, the stimulus of cheerful, but much more of profane society and conversation, upon the animal spirits, becomes an exciting cause, and, like the stroke of the flint upon the steel, renders the sparks of vice both active and visible. By removing men out of the reach of this exciting cause, they are often reformed, especially if they are confined long enough to produce a sufficient chasm in their habits of vice. Where the benefit of reflection and instruction from books can be added to solitude and confinement, their good effects are still more certain. To this philosophers and poets in every age have assented, by describing the life of a hermit as a life of passive virtue.

11. Connected with solitude, as a mechanical means of promoting virtue, SILENCE deserves to be mentioned in this place. The late Dr. Fothergill, in his plan of education for that benevolent institution at Ackworth, which was the last care of his useful life, says every thing that can be said in favour of

this necessary discipline, in the following words: "To habituate children from their early infancy, to silence and attention, is of the greatest advantage to them, not only as a preparative to their advancement in religious life, but as the groundwork of a well cultivated understanding. To have the active minds of children put under a kind of restraint; to be accustomed to turn their attention from external objects, and habituated to a degree of abstracted quiet, is a matter of great consequence, and lasting benefit to them. Although it cannot be supposed, that young and active minds are always engaged in silence as they ought to be, yet to be accustomed thus to quietness, is no small point gained towards fixing a habit of patience, and recollection, which seldom forsakes those who have been properly instructed in this entrance of the school of wisdom, during the residue of their days."

For the purpose of acquiring this branch of education, children cannot associate too early, nor too often with their parents, or with their superiors in age, rank, and wisdom.

12. The effects of MUSIC upon the moral faculty, have been felt and recorded in every country. Hence we are able to discover the virtues and vices of different nations, by their tunes, as certainly as by their laws. The effects of music, when simply mechanical, upon the passions, are powerful and extensive. But it remains yet to determine the degrees of moral ecstacy,[** sic] that may be produced by an attack upon the ear, the reason, and the moral principle, at the same time, by the combined powers of music and eloquence.

13. The ELOQUENCE of the PULPIT is nearly allied to music in its effects upon the moral faculty. It is true, there can be no permanent change in the temper, and moral conduct of a man, that is not derived from the understanding and the will; but we must remember, that these two powers of the mind are most assailable, when they are attacked through the avenue of the passions; and these, we know, when agitated by the powers of eloquence, exert a mechanical action upon every power of the soul. Hence we find in every age and country, where christianity has been propagated, the most accomplished orators have generally been the most successful reformers of mankind. There must be a defect of eloquence in a preacher, who, with the resources for oratory, which are contained in the Old and New Testaments, does not produce in every man who hears him, at least a temporary love of virtue. I grant that the eloquence of the pulpit alone cannot change men into christians, but it certainly possesses the power of changing brutes into men. Could the eloquence of the stage be properly directed, it is impossible to conceive the extent of its mechanical effects upon morals. The language and imagery of a Shakespeare, upon moral and religious subjects, poured upon the passions and the senses, in all the beauty and variety of dramatic representation; who could resist, or describe their effects?

14. ODOURS of various kinds have been observed to act in the most sensible manner upon the moral faculty. Brydone tells us, upon the authority of a celebrated philosopher in Italy, that the peculiar wickedness of the people who live in the neighbourhood of Ætna and Vesuvius, is occasioned chiefly by the smell of the sulphur and of the hot exhalations which are constantly discharged from those volcanos. Agreeable odours seldom fail to inspire serenity, and to compose the angry spirits. Hence the pleasure, and one of the advantages of a flower garden. The smoke of tobacco is likewise of a composing nature, and tends not only to produce what is called a train in perception, but to hush the agitated passions into silence and order. Hence the practice of connecting the pipe or segar, and the bottle together, in public company.

15. It will be sufficient only to mention LIGHT and DARKNESS, to suggest facts in favour of the influence of each of them upon moral sensibility. How often do the peevish complaints of the night in sickness, give way to the composing rays of the light of the morning? Othello cannot murder Desdemona by candle-light, and who has not felt the effects of a blazing fire upon the gentle passions?

16. It is to be lamented, that no experiments have as yet been made, to determine the effects of all the different species of AIRS, which chemistry has lately discovered, upon the moral faculty. I have authority from actual experiments, only to declare, that dephlogisticated air, when taken into the lungs, produces cheerfulness, gentleness, and serenity of mind.

17. What shall we say of the effects of MEDICINES upon the moral faculty? That many substances in the materia medica act upon the intellects, is well known to physicians. Why should it be thought impossible for medicines to act in like manner upon the moral faculty? May not the earth contain, in its bowels, or upon its surface, antidotes? But I will not blend facts with conjectures. Clouds and darkness still hang upon this part of my subject.

Let it not be suspected, from any thing that I have delivered, that I suppose the influence of physical causes upon the moral faculty, renders the agency of divine influence unnecessary to our moral happiness. I only maintain, that the operations of the divine government are carried on in the moral, as in the natural world, by the instrumentality of second causes. I have only trodden in the footsteps of the inspired writers; for most of the physical causes I have enumerated, are connected with moral precepts, or have been used as the means of reformation from vice, in the Old and New Testaments. To the cases that have been mentioned, I shall only add, that Nebuchadnezzar was cured of his pride, by means of solitude and a vegetable diet. Saul was cured of his evil spirit, by means of David's harp, and St. Paul expressly says, "I keep my body under, and bring it into subjection, lest that by any means, when I have preached to others, I myself should be a castaway." But I will go one step further, and add in favour of divine influence upon the moral principle, that in those extraordinary cases, where bad men are suddenly reformed, without the instrumentality of physical, moral, or rational causes, I believe that the organization of those parts of the body, in which the faculties of the mind are seated, undergoes a physical change[11]; and hence the expression of a "new creature," which is made use of in the Scriptures to denote this change, is proper in a literal, as well as a figurative sense. It is probably the beginning of that perfect renovation of the human body, which is predicted by St. Paul in the following words: "For our conversation is in heaven, from whence we look for the Saviour, who shall change our vile bodies, that they may be fashioned according to his own glorious body." I shall not pause to defend myself against the charge of enthusiasm in this place; for the age is at length arrived, so devoutly wished for by Dr. Cheyne, in which men will not be deterred in their researches after truth, by the terror of odious or unpopular names.

I cannot help remarking under this head, that if the conditions of those parts of the human body which are connected with the human soul, influence morals, the same reason may be given for a virtuous education, that has been admitted for teaching music and the pronunciation of foreign languages, in the early and yielding state of those organs which form the voice and speech. Such is the effect of a moral education, that we often see its fruits in advanced stages of life, after the religious principles which were connected with it, have been renounced; just as we perceive the same care in a surgeon in his attendance upon patients, after the sympathy which first produced this care, has ceased to operate upon his mind. The boasted morality of the deists, is, I believe, in most cases, the offspring of habits, produced originally by the principles and precepts of christianity. Hence appears the wisdom of Solomon's advice, "Train up a child in the way he should go, and when he is old he will not," I had almost said, he cannot "depart from it."

Thus have I enumerated the principal causes which act mechanically upon morals. If from the combined action of physical powers that are opposed to each other, the moral faculty should become stationary, or if the virtue or vice produced by them, should form a neutral quality, composed of both of them, I hope it will not call in question the truth of our general propositions. I have only mentioned the effects of physical causes in a simple state[12].

It might help to enlarge our ideas upon this subject, to take notice of the influence of the different stages of society, of agriculture and commerce, of soil and situation, of the different degrees of cultivation of taste, and of the intellectual powers, of the different forms of government, and lastly, of the different professions and occupations of mankind, upon the moral faculty; but as these act indirectly only, and by the intervention of causes that are unconnected with matter, I conceive they are foreign to the business of the present inquiry. If they should vary the action of the simple physical causes in any degree, I hope it will not call in question the truth of our general propositions, any more than the compound action of physical powers, that are opposed to each other. There remain but a few more causes which are of a compound nature, but they are so nearly related to those which are purely mechanical, that I shall beg leave to trespass upon your patience, by giving them a place in my oration.

The effects of imitation, habit, and association upon morals, would furnish ample matter for investigation. Considering how much the shape, texture, and conditions of the human body, influence morals, I submit it to the consideration of the ingenious, whether, in our endeavours to imitate moral examples, some advantage may not be derived, from our copying the features and external manners of the originals. What makes the success of this experiment probable is, that we generally find men, whose faces resemble each other, have the same manners and dispositions. I infer the possibility of success in an attempt to imitate originals in a manner that has been mentioned, from the facility with which domestics acquire a resemblance to their masters and mistresses, not only in manners, but in countenance, in those cases where they are tied to them by respect and affection. Husbands and wives also, where they possess the same species of face, under circumstances of mutual attachment, often acquire a resemblance to each other.

From the general detestation in which hypocrisy is held, both by good and bad men, the mechanical effects of habit upon virtue have not been sufficiently explored. There are, I am persuaded, many instances where virtues have been assumed by accident, or necessity, which have become real from habit, and afterwards derived their nourishment from the heart. Hence the propriety of Hamlet's advice to his mother:

"Assume a virtue, if you have it not.That monster, Custom, who all sense doth eatOf habits evil, is angel yet in this,That to the use of actions fair and goodHe likewise gives a frock or livery,That aptly is put on. Refrain to-night,And that shall lend a kind of easinessTo the next abstinence; the next more easy:For use can almost change the stamp of nature,And master even the devil, or throw him out,With wondrous potency."

The influence of ASSOCIATION upon morals, opens an ample field for inquiry. It is from this principle, that we explain the reformation from theft and drunkenness in servants, which we sometimes see produced by a draught of spirits, in which tartar emetic had been secretly dissolved. The recollection of the pain and sickness excited by the emetic, naturally associates itself with the spirits, so as to render them both equally the objects of aversion. It is by calling in this principle only, that we can account for the conduct of Moses, in grinding the golden calf into a powder, and afterwards dissolving it (probably by means of hepar sulphuris) in water, and compelling the children of Israel to drink of it, as a punishment for their idolatry. This mixture is bitter and nauseating in the highest degree. An inclination to idolatry, therefore, could not be felt without being associated with the remembrance of this disagreeable mixture, and of course being rejected, with equal abhorrence. The benefit of corporal punishments, when they are of a short duration, depends in part upon their being connected, by time and place, with the crimes for which they are inflicted. Quick as the thunder follows the lightning, if it were possible, should punishments follow the crimes, and the advantage of association would be more certain, if the spot where they were committed, were made the theatre of their expiation. It is from the effects of this association, probably, that the change of place and company, produced by exile and transportation, has so often reclaimed bad men, after moral, rational, and physical means of reformation had been used to no purpose.

As SENSIBILITY is the avenue to the moral faculty, every thing which tends to diminish it tends also to injure morals. The Romans owed much of their corruption to the sights of the contests of their gladiators, and of criminals, with wild beasts. For these reasons, executions should never be public. Indeed, I believe there are no public punishments of any kind, that do not harden the hearts of spectators, and thereby lessen the natural horror which all crimes at first excite in the human mind.

CRUELTY to brute animals is another means of destroying moral sensibility. The ferocity of savages has been ascribed in part to their peculiar mode of subsistence. Mr. Hogarth points out, in his ingenious prints, the connection between cruelty to brute animals in youth, and murder in manhood. The emperor Domitian prepared his mind, by the amusement of killing flies, for all those bloody crimes which afterwards disgraced his reign. I am so perfectly satisfied of the truth of a connection between morals and humanity to brutes, that I shall find it difficult to restrain my idolatry for that legislature, that shall first establish a system of laws, to defend them from outrage and oppression.

In order to preserve the vigour of the moral faculty, it is of the utmost consequence to keep young people as ignorant as possible of those crimes that are generally thought most disgraceful to human nature. Suicide, I believe, is often propagated by means of newspapers. For this reason, I should be glad to see the proceedings of our courts kept from the public eye, when they expose or punish monstrous vices.

The last mechanical method of promoting morality that I shall mention, is to keep sensibility alive, by a familiarity with scenes of distress from poverty and disease. Compassion never awakens in the human bosom, without being accompanied by a train of sister virtues. Hence the wise man justly remarks, that "By the sadness of the countenance, the heart is made better."

A late French writer, in his prediction of events that are to happen in the year 4000, says, "That mankind in that æra shall be so far improved by religion and government, that the sick and the dying shall no longer be thrown, together with the dead, into splendid houses, but shall be relieved and protected in a connection with their families and society." For the honour of humanity, an institution[13], destined for that distant period, has lately been founded in this city, that shall perpetuate the year 1786 in the history of Pennsylvania. Here the feeling heart, the tearful eye, and the charitable hand, may always be connected together, and the flame of sympathy, instead of being extinguished in taxes, or expiring in a solitary blaze by a single contribution, may be kept alive, by constant exercise. There is a necessary connection between animal sympathy, and good morals. The priest and the Levite, in the New Testament, would probably have relieved the poor man who fell among thieves, had accident brought them near enough to his wounds. The unfortunate Mrs. Bellamy was rescued from the dreadful purpose of drowning herself, by nothing but the distress of a child, rending the air with its cries for bread. It is probably owing, in some measure, to the connection between good morals and sympathy that the fair sex, in every age and country, have been more distinguished for virtue, than men; for how seldom do we hear of a woman, devoid of humanity?

Lastly, ATTRACTION, COMPOSITION, and DECOMPOSITION, belong to the passions as well as to matter. Vices of the same species attract each other with the most force: hence the bad consequences of crowding young men, whose propensities are generally the same, under one roof, in our modern plans of education. The effects of composition and decomposition upon vices, appear in the meanness of the school-boy being often cured by the prodigality of a military life, and by the precipitation of avarice, which is often produced by ambition and love.

If physical causes influence morals in the manner we have described, may they not also influence religious principles and opinions? I answer in the affirmative; and I have authority, from the records of physic, as well as from my own observations, to declare, that religious melancholy and madness, in all their variety of species, yield with more facility to medicine, than simply to polemical discourses, or to casuistical advice. But this subject is foreign to the business of the present inquiry.

From a review of our subject, we are led to contemplate with admiration, the curious structure of the human mind. How distinct are the number, and yet how united! How subordinate, and yet how co-equal are all its faculties! How wonderful is the action of the mind upon the body! of the body upon the mind! and of the Divine Spirit upon both! What a mystery is the mind of man to itself!——O! Nature!——or, to speak more properly, O! THOU GOD OF NATURE! in vain do we attempt to scan THY immensity, or to comprehend THY various modes of existence, when a single particle of light, issued from THYSELF, and kindled into intelligence in the bosom of man, thus dazzles and confounds our understandings!

The extent of the moral powers and habits in man is unknown. It is not improbable, but the human mind contains principles of virtue, which have never yet been excited into action. We behold with surprise the versatility of the human body in the exploits of tumblers and rope-dancers. Even the agility of a wild beast has been demonstrated in a girl of France, and an amphibious nature has been discovered in the human species, in a young man in Spain. We listen with astonishment to the accounts of the *memories* of Mithridates, Cyrus, and Servin. We feel a veneration bordering upon divine homage, in contemplating the stupenduous *understandings* of lord Verulam and sir Isaac Newton; and our eyes grow dim, in attempting to pursue Shakespeare and Milton in their immeasurable flights of *imagination*. And if the history of mankind does not furnish similar instances of the versatility and perfection of our species in virtue, it is because the moral faculty has been the subject of less culture and fewer experiments than the body, and the intellectual faculties of the mind. From what has been said, the reason of this is obvious. Hitherto the cultivation of the moral faculty has been the business of parents, schoolmasters, and divines[14]. But if the principles, we have laid down, be just, the improvement and extension of this principle should be equally the business of the legislator, the natural philosopher, and the physician; and a physical regimen should as necessarily accompany a moral precept, as directions with respect to the air, exercise, and diet, generally accompany prescriptions for the consumption, and the gout. To encourage us to undertake experiments for the improvement of morals, let us recollect the success of philosophy in lessening the number, and mitigating the violence of incurable diseases. The intermitting fever, which proved fatal to two of the monarchs of Britain, is now under absolute subjection to medicine. Continual fevers are much less fatal than formerly. The small-pox is disarmed of its mortality by inoculation, and even the tetanus and the cancer have lately received a check in their ravages upon mankind. But medicine has done more. It has penetrated the deep and gloomy abyss of death, and acquired fresh honours in his cold embraces. Witness the many hundred people who have lately been brought back to life by the successful efforts of the humane societies, which are now established in many parts of Europe, and in some parts of America. Should the same industry and ingenuity, which have produced these triumphs of medicine over diseases and death, be applied to the moral science, it is highly probable, that most of those baneful vices, which deform the human breast, and convulse the nations of the earth, might be banished from the world. I am not so sanguine as to suppose, that it is possible for man to acquire so much perfection from science, religion, liberty, and good government, as to cease to be mortal; but I am fully persuaded, that from the combined action of causes, which operate at once upon the reason, the moral faculty, the passions, the senses, the brain, the nerves, the blood, and the heart, it is possible to produce such a change in his moral character, as shall raise him to a resemblance of angels; nay, more, to the likeness of GOD himself. The state of Pennsylvania still deplores the loss of a man, in whom not only reason and revelation, but many of the physical causes that have been enumerated, concurred to produce such attainments in moral excellency, as have seldom appeared in a human being. This amiable citizen considered his fellow-creature, man, as God's extract, from his own works; and whether this image of himself was cut out from ebony or copper; whether he spoke his own, or a foreign language; or whether he worshipped his Maker with ceremonies, or without them, he still considered him as a brother, and equally the object of his benevolence. Poets and historians, who are to live hereafter, to you I commit his panegyric; and when you hear of a law for abolishing slavery in each of the American states, such as was passed in Pennsylvania, in the year 1780; when you hear of the kings and queens of Europe, publishing edicts for abolishing the trade in human souls; and, lastly, when you hear of schools and churches, with all the arts of civilized life, being established among the nations of Africa, then remember and record, that this revolution in favour of human happiness, was the effect of the labours, the publications, the private letters, and the prayers of ANTHONY BENEZET[15].

I return from this digression, to address myself in a particular manner to you, VENERABLE SAGES and FELLOW CITIZENS in the REPUBLIC OF LETTERS. The influence of philosophy, we have been told, has already been felt in courts. To increase, and complete this influence, there is nothing more necessary, than for the numerous literary societies in Europe and America, to add the SCIENCE OF MORALS to their experiments and inquiries. The godlike scheme of Henry IV, of France, and of the illustrious queen Elizabeth, of England, for establishing a perpetual peace in Europe, may be accomplished without a system of jurisprudence, by a confederation of learned men, and learned societies. It is in their power, by multiplying the objects of human reason, to bring the monarchs and rulers of the world under their subjection, and thereby to extirpate war, slavery, and capital punishments, from the list of human evils. Let it not be suspected that I detract, by this declaration, from the honour of the Christian religion. It is true, Christianity was propagated without the aid of human learning; but this was one of those miracles, which was necessary to establish it, and which, by repetition, would cease to be a miracle. They misrepresent the Christian religion, who suppose it to be wholly an internal revelation, and addressed only to the moral faculties of the mind. The truths of Christianity afford the greatest scope for the human understanding, and they will become intelligible to us, only in proportion as the human genius is stretched, by means of philosophy, to its utmost dimensions. Errors may be opposed to errors; but truths, upon all subjects, mutually support each other. And perhaps one reason why some parts of the Christian revelation are still involved in obscurity, may be occasioned by our imperfect knowledge of the phenomena and laws of nature. The truths of philosophy and Christianity dwell alike in the mind of the Deity, and reason and religion are equally the offspring of his goodness. They must, therefore, stand and fall together. By reason, in the present instance, I mean the power of judging of truth, as well as the power of comprehending it. Happy æra! when the divine and the philosopher shall embrace each other, and unite their labours for the reformation and happiness of mankind!

ILLUSTRIOUS COUNSELLORS and SENATORS of Pennsylvania[16]! I anticipate your candid reception of this feeble effort to increase the quantity of virtue in our republic. It is not my business to remind you of the immense resources for greatness, which nature and Providence have bestowed upon our state. Every advantage which France has derived from being placed in the centre of Europe, and which Britain has derived from her mixture of nations, Pennsylvania has opened to her. But my business, at present, is to suggest the means of promoting the happiness, not the greatness, of the state. For this purpose, it is absolutely necessary that our government, which unites into one, all the minds of the state, should possess, in an eminent degree, not only the understanding, the passions, and the will, but, above all, the moral faculty and the conscience of an individual. Nothing can be politically right, that is morally wrong; and no necessity can ever sanctify a law, that is contrary to equity. VIRTUE is the soul of a republic. To promote this, laws for the suppression of vice and immorality will be as ineffectual, as the increase and enlargement of jails. There is but one method of preventing crimes, and of rendering a republican form of government durable, and that is, by disseminating the seeds of virtue and knowledge through every part of the state, by means of proper modes and places of education, and this can be done effectually only by the interference and aid of the legislature. I am so deeply impressed with the truth of this opinion, that were this evening to be the last of my life, I would not only say to the asylum of my ancestors, and my beloved native country, with the patriot of Venice, "Esto perpetua," but I would add, as the last proof of my affection for her, my parting advice to the guardians of her liberties, "To establish and support PUBLIC SCHOOLS, in every part of the state."

Footnotes:

[1] Rom. i. 14, 15.

[2] Oration pro Milne.

[3] Vol. III. p. 216, 217.

[4] Milton seems to have been of this opinion. Hence, after ascribing repentance to Satan, he makes him declare,

"Farewell remorse: all good to me is lost,*Evil*, be thou my *good*."——
Paradise Lost, Book IV.

[5] I have selected this case from many others, which have come under my notice, in which the moral faculty appeared to be impaired by diseases, particularly by the typhus of Dr. Cullen, and by those species of palsy which affect the brain.

[6] Xenophon makes Cyrus declare, in his last moments, "That the soul of man, at the hour of death, appears *most divine*, and then foresees something of future events."

[7] Essay concerning the Human Understanding, book I. chap. 3.

[8] Mr. Locke.

[9] "Life and immortality *are* brought to light *only* through the gospel." 2 Tim. i. 10.

[10] There is a morbid state of excitability in the body during the convalescence from fever, which is intimately connected with an undue propensity to venereal pleasures. I have met with several instances of it. The marriage of the celebrated Mr. Howard to a woman who was twice as old as himself, and very sickly, has been ascribed, by his biographer, Dr. Aiken, to *gratitude* for her great attention to him in a fit of sickness. I am disposed to ascribe it to a sudden paroxysm of another passion, which, as a religious man, he could not gratify in any other, than in a lawful way. I have heard of two young clergymen who married the women who had nursed them in fits of sickness. In both cases there was great inequality in their years, and condition in life. Their motive was, probably, the same as that which I have attributed to Mr. Howard. Dr. Patrick Russel takes notice of an uncommon degree of

venereal excitability which followed attacks of the plague at Messina, in 1743, in all ranks of people. Marriages, he says, were more frequent after it than usual, and virgins were, in some instances, violated, who died of that disease, by persons who had just recovered from it.

[11] St. Paul was suddenly transformed from a persecutor into a man of a gentle and amiable spirit. The manner in which this change was effected upon his mind, he tells us in the following words: "Neither circumcision availeth any thing, nor uncircumcision, but a new creature. From henceforth let no man trouble me; for I bear in *my body*, the *marks* of our Lord Jesus." Galatians, vi. 15, 17.

[12] The doctrine of the influence of physical causes on morals is happily calculated to beget charity towards the failings of our fellow-creatures. Our duty to practise this virtue is enforced by motives drawn from science, as well as from the precepts of christianity.

[13] A public dispensary.

[14] The people commonly called Quakers and the Methodists, make use of the greatest number of physical remedies in their religious and moral discipline, of any sects of Christians; and hence we find them every where distinguished for their good morals. There are several excellent *physical* institutions in other churches; and if they do not produce the same moral effects that we observe from physical institutions among those two modern sects, it must be ascribed to their being more neglected by the members of those churches.

[15] This worthy man was descended from an ancient and honourable family that flourished in the court of Louis XIV. With liberal prospects in life he early devoted himself to teaching an English school; in which, for industry, capacity, and attention to the morals and principles of the youth committed to his care, he was without an equal. He published many excellent tracts against the African trade, against war, and the use of spiritous liquors, and one in favour of civilizing and Christianizing the Indians. He wrote to the queen of Great Britain, and the queen of Portugal, to use their influence in their respective courts to abolish the African trade. He also wrote an affectionate letter to the king of Prussia, to dissuade him from making war. The history of his life affords a remarkable instance how much it is possible for an individual to accomplish in the world; and that the most humble stations do not preclude good men from the most extensive usefulness. He bequeathed his estate (after the death of his widow) to the support of a school for the education of negro children, which he had founded and taught for several years before he died. He departed this life in May, 1784, in the 71st year of his age, in the meridian of his usefulness, universally lamented by persons of all ranks and denominations.

[16] The president, and supreme executive council, and the members of the general assembly of Pennsylvania, attended the delivery of the oration, in the hall of the university, by invitation from the Philosophical Society.

AN INQUIRY
INTO THE
CAUSES AND CURE
OF THE
PULMONARY CONSUMPTION.

In an essay, entitled "Thoughts on the Pulmonary Consumption[17]," I attempted to show that this disease was the effect of causes which induced general debility, and that the only hope of discovering a cure for it should be directed to such remedies as act upon the whole system. In the following inquiry, I shall endeavour to establish the truth of each of those opinions, by a detail of facts and reasonings, at which I only hinted in my former essay.

The method I have chosen for this purpose, is to deliver, and afterwards to support, a few general propositions.

I shall begin by remarking,

I. That the pulmonary consumption is induced by predisposing debility.

This I infer, 1st, From the remote and exciting causes which produce it. The remote causes are pneumony, catarrh, hæmoptysis, rheumatism, gout, asthma, scrophula, chronic diseases of the stomach, liver, and kidneys, nervous and intermitting fevers, measles, repelled humours from the surface of the body, the venereal disease, obstructed menses, sudden growth about the age of puberty, grief, and all other debilitating passions of the mind; hypochondriasis, improper lactation, excessive evacuation of all kinds, more especially by stool[18], cold and damp air, a cough, external violence acting upon the body[19]; and finally, every thing that tends, directly or indirectly, to diminish the strength of the system.

The most frequent exciting cause of consumption is the alternate application of heat and cold to the whole external surface of the body; but all the remote causes which have been enumerated, operate as exciting causes of consumption, when they act on previous debility. Original injuries of the lungs seldom excite this disease, except they first induce a debility of the whole system, by a troublesome and obstinate cough.

2. From the debilitating occupations and habits of persons who are most liable to this disease. These are studious men, and mechanics who lead

sedentary lives in confined places; also women, and all persons of irritable habits, whether of body or mind.

3. From the period in which persons are most liable to be affected by this disease. This is generally between the 18th and 36th year of life, a period in which the system is liable, in a peculiar manner, to most diseases which induce it, and in which there is a greater expenditure of strength, than in any other stage of life, by the excessive exercises of the body and mind, in the pursuits of business or pleasure.

I have conformed to authors, in fixing the period of consumptions between the 18th and 36th year of life; but it is well known that it sometimes appears in children, and frequently in persons beyond the 40th, or even 60th year of life.

II. The pulmonary consumption is a primary disease of the *whole* system. This I infer,

1. From the causes which produce it, acting upon the whole system.

2. From the symptoms of general debility which always precede the affection of the lungs. These symptoms are a quick pulse, especially towards evening; a heat and burning in the palms of the hands; faintness, head-ach, sickness at stomach, and an occasional diarrhœa. I have frequently observed each of these symptoms for several months before I have heard of a single complaint in the breast.

3. From the pulmonary consumption alternating with other diseases which obviously belong to the whole system. I shall briefly mention these diseases.

The RHEUMATISM. I have seen many cases in which this disease and the consumption have alternately, in different seasons or years, affected the system. In the winter of 1792, three clinical patients in the Pennsylvania hospital exemplified by their complaints the truth of this observation. They were relieved several times of a cough by rheumatic pains in their limbs, which seemed for a while to promise a cure to their pulmonic complaints.

The GOUT has often been observed to alternate with the pulmonary consumption, especially in persons in the decline of life. Dr. Sydenham describes a short cough continuing through the whole winter, as a symptom of gouty habits. A gentleman from Virginia died under my care in the spring of 1788, in the 45th year of his age, with all the symptoms of pulmonary consumption, which had frequently alternated with pains and a swelling in his feet.

The pulmonary consumption has been observed to alternate with MADNESS. Of this I have seen two instances, in both of which the cough and expectoration were wholly suspended during the continuance of the derangement of the mind. Dr. Mead mentions a melancholy case of the same kind in a young lady, and similar cases are to be met with in other authors. In all of them the disease proved fatal. In one of the cases which came under my notice, the symptoms of consumption returned before the death of the patient.

I have likewise witnessed two cases in which the return of reason after madness, was suddenly succeeded by a fatal pulmonary consumption. Perhaps the false hopes, and even the cheerfulness which so universally occur in this disease, may be resolved into a morbid state of the mind, produced by a general derangement of the whole system. So universal are the delusion and hopes of patients, with respect to the nature and issue of this disease, that I have never met with but one man, who, upon being asked what was the matter with him, answered unequivocally, "that he was in a consumption."

Again: Dr. Bennet mentions a case of "A phthisical patient, who was seized with a violent PAIN IN THE TEETH for two days, and in whom, during that time, every symptom of a consumption, except the leanness of the body, altogether vanished:" and he adds further, "that a defluction on the lungs had often been relieved by SALIVARY EVACUATIONS[20]."

I have seen several instances in which the pulmonary symptoms have alternated with HEADACH and DYSPEPSIA; also with pain and noise in one EAR. This affection of the ears sometimes continues throughout the whole disease, without any remission of the pulmonary symptoms. I have seen one case of a discharge of matter from the left ear, without being accompanied by either pain or noise.

In all our books of medicine are to be found cases of consumption alternating with ERUPTIONS ON THE SKIN.

And who has not seen the pulmonary symptoms alternately relieved and reproduced by the appearance or cessation of a diarrhœa, or pains in the BOWELS?

To these facts I shall only add, under this head, as a proof of the consumption being a disease of the whole system, that it is always more or less relieved by the change which is induced in the system by pregnancy.

4. I infer that the pulmonary consumption is a disease of the whole system from its analogy with several other diseases, which, though accompanied by

local affections, are obviously produced by a morbid state of the whole system.

The rheumatism, the gout, the measles, small-pox, the different species of cynanche, all furnish examples of the connection of local affections with a general disease; but the APOPLEXY, and the PNEUMONY, furnish the most striking analogies of local affection, succeeding a general disease of the system in the pulmonary consumption.

The most frequent predisposing cause of apoplexy is a general debility of the system, produced by intemperance in eating and drinking. The phenomena of the disease are produced by an effusion of blood or serum, in consequence of a morbid distension, or of a rupture of the vessels of the brain. The pulmonary consumption begins and ends in the same way, allowing only for the difference of situation and structure of the brain and lungs. After the production of predisposing debility from the action of the remote causes formerly enumerated, the fluids are determined to the weakest part of the body. Hence effusions of serum or blood take place in the lungs. When serum is effused, a pituitous or purulent expectoration alone takes place; when blood is discharged, a disease is produced which has been called hæmoptysis. An effusion of blood in the brain, brought on by the operation of general debility, has been called by Dr. Hoffman, with equal propriety, a hæmorrhage of the brain. The effusion of blood in the lungs, in consequence of the rupture of a blood-vessel, is less fatal than the same accident when it occurs in the brain, only because the blood in the former case is more easily discharged from the system. Where no rupture of a blood-vessel is produced, death is nearly as speedy and certain in the one case as in the other. Dissections show many cases of suffocation and death, from the lungs being preternaturally filled with blood or serum. From this great analogy between the remote and proximate causes of the two diseases which have been described, I have taken the liberty to call them both by the name of apoplexy. The only symptom which does not accord with the derivation of the term, is, that in the apoplexy of the lungs, the patient does not fall down as if by an external stroke, which is most frequently the case in the apoplexy of the brain.

The history of the remote and proximate causes of pneumony will furnish us with a still more remarkable analogy of the connection between a *local* affection, and a *general* disease of the system. The pneumony is produced by remote exciting causes which act on the whole system. The whole arterial system is frequently agitated by a fever in this disease before a pain is perceived in the breast or sides, and this fever generally constitutes its strength and danger. The expectoration which terminates the disease in health, is always the effect of effusions produced by a general disease, and even the vomicas, which sometimes succeed a deficiency of bleeding, always depend upon the same general cause. From this view of the analogy between pneumony and pulmonary consumption, it would seem that the two diseases differed from each other only by the shorter or longer operation of the causes which induce them, and by the greater or less violence and duration of their symptoms. The pneumony appears to be an *acute* consumption, and the consumption a *chronic* pneumony. From the analogy of the pulmonary consumption with the diminutive term of certain fevers, I have taken the liberty of calling it a PNEUMONICULA.

5. I infer that the pulmonary consumption is a disease of the whole system, from its existence without ulcers in the lungs. Of this there are many cases recorded in books of medicine.

Dr. Leigh informs us, in his Natural History of Lancashire, that the consumption was a very common disease on the sea coast of that country; but that it was not accompanied either by previous inflammation or ulcers in the lungs. It was generally attended, he says, by an unusual peevishness of temper.

6. I infer that the pulmonary consumption is a disease of the whole system, from its being relieved, or cured, only by remedies which act upon the whole system. This will appear, I hope, hereafter, when we come to treat of the cure of this disease.

Let us now enquire how far the principles I have laid down will apply to the supposed causes of consumption. These causes have been said to be, an abscess in the lungs, hæmoptysis, tubercles, without and with ulcers, catarrh, hereditary diathesis, contagion, and the matter of cutaneous eruptions, or sores repelled, and thrown upon the lungs. I shall make a few observations upon each of them.

1. An abscess in the lungs is generally the consequence of a neglected, or half-cured pneumony. It is seldom fatal, where it is not connected with a predisposition to consumption from general debility, or where general debility is not previously induced by the want of appetite, sleep, and exercise, which sometimes accompany that disease of the lungs. This explanation of the production of consumption by an abscess in the lungs, will receive further support from attending to the effects of wounds in the lungs. How seldom are they followed by pulmonary consumption; and this only because they are as seldom accompanied by predisposing general debility. I do not recollect a single instance of this disease having followed a wound in the lungs, either by the bayonet, or a bullet, during our revolutionary war. The recoveries which have succeeded such wounds, and frequently under the

most unfavourable circumstances, show how very improbable it is that a much slighter affection of the lungs should become the cause of a pulmonary consumption.

A British officer, whom I met in the British camp, a few days after the battle of Brandywine, in September, 1777, informed me that the surgeon-general of the royal army had assured him, that out of twenty-four soldiers who had been admitted into the hospitals, during the campaign of 1776, with wounds in their lungs, twenty-three of them had recovered. Even primary diseases of the lungs often exist with peculiar violence, or continue for many years without inducing a consumption. I have never known but one instance of the whooping-cough ending in consumption, and all our books of medicine contain records of the asthma continuing for twenty and thirty years without terminating in that disease. The reason in both cases, must be ascribed to those two original diseases of the lungs not being accompanied by general debility. One fact more will serve to throw still further light upon the subject. Millers are much afflicted with a cough from floating particles of flour constantly irritating their lungs, and yet they are not more subject to consumptions than other labouring people. Hence "a miller's cough" is proverbial in some places, to denote a cough of long continuance without danger.

2. The hæmoptysis is either a local disease, or it is the effect of general debility of the whole system. When it is local, or when it is the effect of causes which induce a *temporary* or *acute* debility only in the system, it is seldom followed by consumption. The accidental discharge of blood from the lungs, from injuries, and from an obstruction of the menses in women is of this kind. Many persons are affected by this species of hæmorrhage once or twice in their lives, without suffering any inconvenience from it afterwards. I have met with several cases in which it has occurred for many years every time the body was exposed to any of the causes which induce *sudden* debility, and yet no consumption has followed it. The late king of Prussia informed Dr. Zimmerman that he had been frequently attacked by it during his seven years war, and yet he lived, notwithstanding, above twenty years afterwards without any pulmonary complaints. It is only in persons who labour under *chronic* debility, that a hæmoptysis is necessarily followed by consumption.

3. I yield to the popular mode of expression when I speak of a consumption being produced by tubercles. But I maintain that they are the *effects* of general debility communicated to the bronchial vessels which cause them to secrete a preternatural quantity of mucus. This mucus is sometimes poured into the trachea from whence it is discharged by hawking, more especially in the morning; for it is secreted more copiously during the languid hours of sleep than in the day time. But this mucus is frequently secreted into the substance of the lungs, where it produces those tumours we call tubercles.

When this occurs, there is either no cough[21] or a very dry one. That tubercles are formed in this way, I infer from the dissections and experiments of Dr. Stark[22], who tells us, that he found them to consist of inorganic matter; that he was unable to discover any connection between them and the pulmonary vessels, by means of the microscope or injections; and that they first opened into the trachea through the bronchial vessels. It is remarkable that the colour and consistence of the matter of which they are composed, is nearly the same as the matter which is discharged through the trachea, in the moist cough which occurs from a relaxation of the bronchial vessels, and which has been called by Dr. Beddoes a bronchial gleet.

I am aware that these tumours in the lungs have been ascribed to scrophula. But the frequent occurrence of consumptions in persons in whom no scrophulous taint existed, is sufficient to refute this opinion. I have frequently directed my inquiries after this disease in consumptive patients, and have met with very few cases which were produced by it. It is probable that it may frequently be a predisposing cause of consumption in Great Britain, but I am sure it is not in the United States. Baron Humboldt informed me, that the scrophula is unknown in Mexico, and yet consumptions, he said, are very common in that part of North-America. That tubercles are the effects, and not the cause of pulmonary consumption, is further evident from similar tumours being suddenly formed on the intestines by the dysentery, and on the omentum by a yellow fever. Cases of the former are to be met with in the dissections of Sir John Pringle, and one of the latter is mentioned by Dr. Mackittrick, in his inaugural dissertation upon the yellow fever, published in Edinburgh in the year 1766[23].

4. The catarrh is of two kinds, acute and chronic, both of which are connected with general debility, but this debility is most obvious in the chronic catarrh: hence we find it increased by every thing which acts upon the whole system, such as cold and damp weather, fatigue, and, above all, by old age, and relieved or cured by exercise, and every thing else which invigorates the whole system. This species of catarrh often continues for twenty or thirty years without inducing pulmonary consumption, in persons who pursue active occupations.

5. In the hereditary consumption there is either a hereditary debility of the whole system, or a hereditary mal-conformation of the breast. In the latter case, the consumption is the effect of weakness communicated to the whole system, by the long continuance of difficult respiration, or of such injuries being done to the lungs as are incompatible with health and life. It is remarkable, that the consumptive diathesis is more frequently derived from paternal, than maternal ancestors.

6. Physicians, the most distinguished characters, have agreed, that the pulmonary consumption may be communicated by contagion. Under the influence of this belief, Morgagni informs us, that Valsalva, who was predisposed to the consumption, constantly avoided being present at the dissection of the lungs of persons who had died of that disease. In some parts of Spain and Portugal, its contagious nature is so generally believed, that cases of it are reported to the magistrates of those countries, and the clothes of persons who die of it are burned by their orders. The doctrine of nearly all diseases spreading by contagion, required but a short and simple act of the mind, and favoured the indolence and timidity which characterized the old school of medicine. I adopted this opinion, with respect to the consumption, in the early part of my life; but I have lately been led to call its truth in question, especially in the unqualified manner in which it has been taught. In most of the cases in which the disease has been said to be propagated by contagion, its limits are always confined to the members of a single family. Upon examination, I have found them to depend upon some one or more of the following causes:

1. Mal-conformation of the breast, in all the branches of the diseased family. It is not necessary that this organic predisposition should be hereditary.

2. Upon the debility which is incurred by nursing, and the grief which follows the loss of relations who die of it.

3. Upon some local cause undermining the constitutions of a whole family. This may be exhalations from a foul cellar, a privy, or a neighbouring mill-pond, but of so feeble a nature as to produce debility only, with an acute fever, and thus to render the consumption a kind of family epidemic. I was consulted, in the month of August, 1793, by a Mr. Gale, of Maryland, in a pulmonary complaint. He informed me, that he had lost several brothers and sisters with the consumption, and that none of his ancestors had died of it. The deceased persons, five in number, had lived in a place that had been subject to the intermitting fever.

4. Upon some peculiar and unwholesome article of diet, which exerts slowly debilitating effects upon all the branches of a family.

5. Upon a fearful and debilitating apprehension entertained by the surviving members of a family, in which one or two have died of consumption, that they shall perish by the same disease. The effects of all the passions, and especially of fear, acted upon by a lively imagination, in inducing determinations to particular parts of the body, and subsequent disease, are so numerous, as to leave no doubt of the operation of this cause, in producing a number of successive deaths in the same family, from pulmonary consumption.

In favour of its depending upon one or more of the above causes, I shall add two remarks.

1. There is often an interval of from two to ten years, between the sickness and deaths which occur in families from consumptions, and this we know never takes place in any disease which is admitted to be contagious.

2. The consumption is not singular in affecting several branches of a family. I was lately consulted by a young physician from Maryland, who informed me, that two of his brothers, in common with himself, were afflicted with epilepsy. Madness, scrophula, and a disposition to hæmorrhage, often affect, in succession, several branches of the same family; and who will say that any one of the above diseases is propagated by contagion?

The practice of the Spaniards and Portuguese, in burning the clothes of persons who die of consumptions, no more proves the disease to be contagious, than the same acts sanctioned by the advice or orders of public bodies in the United States, establish the contagious nature of the yellow fever. They are, in both countries, marks of the superstition of medicine.

In suggesting these facts, and the inferences which have been drawn from them, I do not mean to deny the possibility of the acrid and fœtid vapour, which is discharged by breathing from an ulcer or abscess in the lungs, nor of the hectic sweats, when rendered putrid by stagnating in sheets, or blankets, communicating this disease to persons who are long exposed to them, by sleeping with consumptive patients; but that such cases rarely occur I infer, from the persons affected often living at a distance from each other, or when they live under the same roof, having no intercourse with the sick. This was the case with the black slaves, who were supposed to have taken the disease from the white branches of a family in Connecticut, and which was mentioned, upon the authority of Dr. Beardsley, in a former edition of this inquiry. Admitting the above morbid matters now and then to act as a remote cause of consumption, it does not militate against the theory I have aimed to establish, for if it follow the analogy of common miasmata and contagions, it must act by first debilitating the whole system. The approach of the jail and bilious fevers is often indicated by general languor. The influenza and the measles are always accompanied by general debility, but the small-pox furnishes an analogy to the case in question more directly in point. The contagion of this disease, whether received by the medium of the air or the skin, never fails of producing weakness in the whole system, before it discovers itself in affections of those parts of the body on which the contagion produced its first operation.

7. I grant that cutaneous humours, and the matter of old sores, when repelled, or suddenly healed, have in some cases fallen upon the lungs, and produced consumption. But I believe, in every case where this has happened, the consumption was preceded by general debility, or that it was not induced, until the whole system had been previously debilitated by a tedious and distressing cough.

If the reasonings founded upon the facts which have been mentioned be just, then it follows,

III. That the abscess, cough, tubercles, ulcers, and purulent or bloody discharges which occur in the pulmonary consumption, are the *effects*, and not the *causes* of the disease; and, that all attempts to cure it, by inquiring after tubercles and ulcers, or into the quality of the discharges from the lungs, are as fruitless as an attempt would be to discover the causes or cure of dropsies, by an examination of the qualities of collections of water, or to find out the causes and cure of fevers, by the quantity or quality of the discharges which take place in those diseases from the kidneys and skin. It is to be lamented, that it is not in pulmonary consumption only, that the effects of a disease have been mistaken for its cause. Water in the brain, a membrane in the trachea, and a preternatural secretion of bile, have been accused of producing hydrocephalus internus, cynanche trachealis, and bilious fever, whereas we now know they are the *effects* of those diseases only, in the successive order in which each of them has been mentioned. It is high time to harness the steeds which drag the car of medicine before, instead of behind it. The earth, in our science, has stood still long enough. Let us at last believe, it revolves round its sun. I admit that the cough, tubercles, and ulcers, after they are formed, increase the danger of a consumption, by becoming new causes of stimulus to the system, but in this they are upon a footing with the water, the membrane, and the bile that have been alluded to, which, though they constitute no part of the diseases that produce them, frequently induce symptoms, and a termination of them, wholly unconnected with the original disease.

The tendency of general debility to produce a disease of the lungs appears in many cases, as well as in the pulmonary consumption. Dr. Lind tells us, that the last stage of the jail fever was often marked by a cough. I have seldom been disappointed in looking for a cough and a copious excretion of mucus and phlegm after the 14th or 15th days of the slow nervous fever. Two cases of hypochondriasis under my care, ended in fatal diseases of the lungs. The debility of old age is generally accompanied by a troublesome cough, and the debility which precedes death, generally discovers its last symptoms in the lungs. Hence most people die with what are called the *rattles*. They are produced by a sudden and copious effusion of mucus in the bronchial vessels of the lungs.

Sometimes the whole force of the consumptive fever falls upon the trachea instead of the lungs, producing in it defluxion, a hawking of blood, and occasionally a considerable discharge of blood, which are often followed by ulcers, and a spitting of pus. I have called it a *tracheal*, instead of a pulmonary consumption. Many people pass through a long life with a mucous defluxion upon the trachea, and enjoy in other respects tolerable health. In such persons the disease is of a local nature. It is only when it is accompanied with debility of the whole system, that it ends in a consumption. Mr. John Harrison, of the Northern Liberties, died of this disease under my care, in the year 1801, in consequence of the discharge of pus from an ulcer which followed a hæmorrhage from the trachea being suddenly suppressed. I have seen another case of the same kind in a lady in this city, in the year 1797. Dr. Spence, of Dumfries, in Virginia, in a letter which I received from him in June, 1805, describes a case then under his care, of this form of consumption. He calls it, very properly, "phthisis trachealis." I have met with two cases of death from this disease, in which there were tubercles in the trachea. The patients breathed with great difficulty, and spoke only in a whisper. One of them died from suffocation. In the other, the tubercle bursted a few days before his death, and discharged a large quantity of fœtid matter.

Should it be asked, why does general debility terminate by a disease in the lungs and trachea, rather than in any other part of the body? I answer, that it seems to be a law of the system, that general debility should always produce some local disease. This local disease sometimes manifests itself in dyspepsia, as in the general debility which follows grief; sometimes it discovers itself in a diarrhœa, as in the general debility which succeeds to fear. Again it appears in the brain, as in the general debility which succeeds intemperance, and the constant or violent exercise of the understanding, or of stimulating passions; but it more frequently appears in the lungs, as the consequence of general debility. It would seem as if the debility in the cases of consumption is seated chiefly in the blood-vessels, while that debility which terminates in diseases of the stomach and bowels, is confined chiefly to the nerves, and that the local affections of the brain arise from a debility, invading alike the nervous and arterial systems. What makes it more probable that the arterial system is *materially* affected in the consumption is, that the disease most frequently occurs in those periods of life, and in those habits in which a peculiar state of irritability or excitability is supposed to be present in the arterial system; also in those climates in which there are the most frequent vicissitudes in the temperature of the weather. It has been observed, that the debility in the inhabitants of the West-Indies, whether produced by the heat of the climate or the excessive pursuits of business or pleasure, generally terminates in dropsy, or in some disease of the alimentary canal.

I have said, that it seemed to be a law of the system, that general debility should always produce some local affection. But to this law there are sometimes exceptions: the atrophy appears to be a consumption without an affection of the lungs. This disease is frequently mentioned by the writers of the 16th and 17th centuries by the name of tabes. I have seen several instances of it in adults, but more in children, and a greater number in the children of black than of white parents. The hectic fever, and even the night sweats, were as obvious in several of these cases, as in those consumptions where general debility had discovered itself in an affection of the lungs.

I come now to make a few observations upon the CURE of consumption; and here I hope it will appear, that the theory which I have delivered admits of an early and very important application to practice.

If the consumption be preceded by general debility, it becomes us to attempt the cure of it before it produce the active symptoms of cough, bloody or purulent discharges from the lungs, and inflammatory or hectic fever. The symptoms which mark its first stage, are too seldom observed; or if observed, they are too often treated with equal neglect by patients and physicians. I shall briefly enumerate these symptoms. They are a slight fever increased by the least exercise; a burning and dryness in the palms of the hands, more especially towards evening; rheumy eyes upon waking from sleep; an increase of urine; a dryness of the skin, more especially of the feet in the morning[24]; an occasional flushing in one, and sometimes in both cheeks; a hoarseness[25]; a slight or acute pain in the breast; a fixed pain in one side, or shooting pains in both sides; head-ache; occasional sick and fainty fits; a deficiency of appetite, and a general indisposition to exercise or motion of every kind.

It would be easy for me to mention cases in which every symptom that has been enumerated has occurred within my own observation. I wish them to be committed to memory by young practitioners; and if they derive the same advantages from attending to them, which I have done, I am sure they will not regret the trouble they have taken for that purpose. It is probable, while a morbid state of the lungs is supposed to be the proximate cause of this disease, they will not derive much reputation or emolument from curing it in its forming stage; but let them remember, that in all attempts to discover the causes and cures of diseases, which have been deemed incurable, a physician will do nothing effectual until he acquire a perfect indifference to his own interest and fame.

The remedies for consumption, in this stage of the disease, are simple and certain. They consist in a desertion of all the remote and exciting causes of the disorder, particularly sedentary employments, damp or cold situations, and whatever tends to weaken the system. When the disease has not yielded to this desertion of its remote and exciting causes, I have recommended the *cold bath*, *steel*, and *bark* with great advantage. However improper, or even dangerous, these remedies may be after the disease assumes an inflammatory or hectic type, and produces an affection of the lungs, they are perfectly safe and extremely useful in the state of the system which has been described. The use of the bark will readily be admitted by all those practitioners who believe the pulmonary consumption to depend upon a scrophulous diathesis. Should even the lungs be affected by scrophulous tumours, it is no objection to the use of the bark, for there is no reason why it should not be as useful in scrophulous tumours of the lungs, as of the glands of the throat, provided it be given before those tumours have produced inflammation; and in this case, no prudent practitioner will ever prescribe it in scrophula, when seated even in the external parts of the body. To these remedies should be added a diet moderately stimulating, and gentle exercise. I shall hereafter mention the different species of exercise, and the manner in which each of them should be used, so as to derive the utmost advantage from them. I can say nothing of the use of salt water or sea air in this stage of the consumption, from my own experience. I have heard them commended by a physician of Rhode-Island; and if they be used before the disease has discovered itself in pulmonary affections, I can easily conceive they may do service.

If the simple remedies which have been mentioned have been neglected, in the first stage of the disease, it generally terminates, in different periods of time, in pulmonary affections, which show themselves under one of the three following forms:

1. A fever, accompanied by a cough, a hard pulse, and a discharge of blood, or mucous matter from the lungs.

2. A fever of the hectic kind, accompanied by chilly fits, and night sweats, and a pulse full, quick, and occasionally hard. The discharges from the lungs, in this state of the disease, are frequently purulent.

3. A fever with a weak frequent pulse, a troublesome cough, and copious purulent discharges from the lungs, a hoarse and weak voice, and chilly fits and night sweats alternating with a diarrhœa.

From this short history of the symptoms of pulmonary consumption there are occasional deviations. I have seen four cases, in which the pulse was natural, or slower than natural, to the last day of life. Mrs. Rebecca Smith, the lovely and accomplished wife of Mr. Robert Smith, of this city, passed through the whole course of this disease, in the year 1802, without a single chilly fit. Two other cases have come under my notice, in which there was not only an absence of chills, but of fever and night sweats. A similar case is recorded in the Memoirs of the Medical Society of London; and lastly, I have seen two cases which terminated fatally, in which there was neither cough nor fever for several months. One of them was in Miss Mary Loxley, the daughter of the late Mr. Benjamin Loxley, in the year 1785. She had complained of a pain in her right side, and had frequent chills with a fever of the hectic kind. They all gave way to frequent and gentle bleedings. In the summer of 1786, she was seized with the same complaints, and as she had great objections to bleeding, she consulted a physician who gratified her, by attempting to cure her by recommending exercise and country air. In the autumn she returned to the city, much worse than when she left it. I was again sent for, and found her confined to her bed with a pain in her right side, but without the least cough or fever. Her pulse was preternaturally slow. She could lie only on her left side. She sometimes complained of acute flying pains in her head, bowels, and limbs. About a month before her death, which was on the 3d of May, 1787, her pulse became quick, and she had a little hecking cough, but without any discharge from her lungs. Upon my first visit to her in the preceding autumn, I told her friends that I believed she had an abscess in her lungs. The want of fever and cough afterwards, however, gave me reason to suspect that I had been mistaken. The morning after her death, I received a message from her father, informing me that it had been among the last requests of his daughter, that the cause of her death should be ascertained, by my opening her body. I complied with this request, and, in company with Dr. Hall, examined her thorax. We found the left lobe of the lungs perfectly sound; the right lobe adhered to the pleura, in separating of which, Dr. Hall plunged his hand into a large sac, which contained about half a pint of purulent matter, and which had nearly destroyed the whole substance of the right lobe of the lungs.

I have never seen a dry tongue in any of the forms or stages of this disease.

The three different forms of the pulmonary affection that I have mentioned, have been distinguished by the names of the first, second, and third stages of the consumption; but as they do not always succeed each other in the order in which they have been mentioned, I shall consider them as different states of the system.

The first I shall call the INFLAMMATORY, the second the HECTIC, and the third the TYPHUS state. I have seen the pulmonary consumption come on sometimes with all the symptoms of the second, and sometimes with most of the symptoms of the third state; and I have seen two cases in which a hard pulse, and other symptoms of inflammatory action, appeared in the last hours of life. It is agreeable to pursue the analogy of this disease with a pneumony, or an acute inflammation of the lungs. They both make their first appearance in the same seasons of the year. It is true, the pneumony most frequently attacks with inflammatory symptoms; but it sometimes occurs with symptoms which forbid blood-letting, and I have more than once seen it attended by symptoms which required the use of wine and bark. The pneumony is attended at first by a dry cough, and an expectoration of streaks of blood; the cough in the consumption, in like manner, is at first dry, and attended by a discharge of blood from the lungs, which is more copious than in the pneumony, only because the lungs are more relaxed in the former than in the latter disease. There are cases of pneumony in which no cough attends. I have just now mentioned that I had seen the absence of that symptom in pulmonary consumption.

The pneumony terminates in different periods, according to the degrees of inflammation, or the nature of the effusions which take place in the lungs: the same observation applies to the pulmonary consumption. The symptoms of the different forms of pneumony frequently run into each other; so do the symptoms of the three forms of consumption which have been mentioned. In short, the pneumony and consumption are alike in so many particulars, that they appear to resemble shadows of the same substance. They differ only as the protracted shadow of the evening does from that of the noon-day sun.

I know that it will be objected here that the consumption is sometimes produced by scrophula, and that this creates an essential difference between it and pneumony. I formerly admitted scrophula to be one of the *remote* causes of the consumption; but this does not invalidate the parallel which has been given of the two diseases. The phenomena produced in the lungs are the same as to their nature, whether they be produced by the remote cause of scrophula, or by the sudden action of cold and heat upon them.

No more happens in the cases of acute and chronic pneumony, than what happens in dysentery and rheumatism. These two last diseases are for the most part so acute, as to confine the patient to his bed or his room, yet we often meet with both of them in patients who go about their ordinary business, and, in some instances, carry their diseases with them for two or three years.

The parallel which has been drawn between the pneumony and consumption, will enable us to understand the reason why the latter disease terminates in such different periods of time. The less it partakes of pneumony, the longer it continues, and vice versa. What is commonly called in this country a *galloping* consumption, is a disease compounded of different degrees of consumption and pneumony. It terminates frequently in two or three months, and without many of the symptoms which usually attend the last stage of pulmonary consumption. But there are cases in which patients in a consumption are suddenly snatched away by an attack of pneumony. I have met with one case only, in which, contrary to my expectation, the patient mended after an attack of an acute inflammation of the lungs, so as to live two years afterwards.

It would seem from these facts, as if nature had preferred a certain gradation in diseases, as well as in other parts of her works. There is scarcely a disease in which there is not a certain number of grades, which mark the distance between health and the lowest specific deviation from it. Each of these grades has received different names, and has been considered as a distinct disease, but more accurate surveys of the animal economy have taught us, that they frequently depend upon the same original causes, and that they are only greater or less degrees of the same disease.

I shall now proceed to say a few words upon the cure of the different states of pulmonary consumption. The remedies for this purpose are of two kinds, viz. PALLIATIVE and RADICAL. I shall first mention the palliative remedies which belong to each state, and then mention those which are alike proper in them all. The palliative remedies for the

I. Or INFLAMMATORY STATE, are

I. BLOOD-LETTING. It may seem strange to recommend this debilitating remedy in a disease brought on by debility. Were it proper in this place, I could prove that there is no disease in which bleeding is prescribed, which is not induced by predisposing debility, in common with the pulmonary consumption. I shall only remark here, that in consequence of the exciting cause acting upon the system (rendered extremely excitable by debility) such a morbid and excessive excitement is produced in the arteries, as to render a diminution of the stimulus of the blood absolutely necessary to reduce it. I have used this remedy with great success, in every case of consumption attended by a hard pulse, or a pulse rendered weak by a laborious transmission of the blood through the lungs. In the months of February and March, in the year 1781, I bled a Methodist minister, who was affected by this state of consumption, fifteen times in the course of six weeks. The quantity of blood drawn at each bleeding was never less than eight ounces, and it was at all times covered with an inflammatory crust. By the addition of country air, and moderate exercise, to this copious evacuation, in the ensuing spring he recovered his health so perfectly, as to discharge all the duties of his profession for many years, nor was he ever afflicted afterwards with a disease in his breast. I have, in another instance, bled a citizen of Philadelphia eight times in two weeks, in this state of consumption, and with the happiest effects. The blood drawn at each bleeding was always sizy, and never less in quantity than ten ounces. Mr. Tracey of Connecticut informed me, in the spring of 1802, that he had been bled eighty-five times in six months, by order of his physician, Dr. Sheldon, in the inflammatory state of this disease. He ascribed his recovery chiefly to this frequent use of the lancet. To these cases I might add many others of consumptive persons who have been perfectly cured by frequent, and of many others whose lives have been prolonged by occasional bleedings. But I am sorry to add, that I could relate many more cases of consumptive patients, who have died martyrs to their prejudices against the use of this invaluable remedy. A common objection to it is, that it has been used without success in this disease. When this has been the case, I suspect that it has been used in one of the other two states of pulmonary consumption which have been mentioned, for it has unfortunately been too fashionable among physicians to prescribe the same remedies in every stage and form of the same disease, and this I take to be the reason why the same medicines, which, in the hands of some physicians, are either inert or instruments of mischief, are, in the hands of others, used with more or less success in every case in which they are prescribed. Another objection to bleeding in the inflammatory state of consumption, is derived from the apparent and even sensible weakness of the patient. The men who urge this objection, do not hesitate to take from sixty to a hundred ounces of blood from a patient in a pneumony, in the course of five or six days, without considering that the debility in the latter case is such as to confine a patient to his bed, while, in the former case, the patient's strength is such as to enable him to walk about his house, and even to attend to his ordinary business. The difference between the debility in the two diseases, consists in its being *acute* in the one, and *chronic* in the other. It is true, the preternatural or convulsive excitement of the arteries is somewhat greater in the pneumony, than in the inflammatory consumption; but the plethora, on which the necessity of bleeding is partly founded, is certainly greater in the inflammatory consumption than in pneumony. This is evident from women, and even nurses, discharging from four to six ounces of menstrual blood every month, while they are labouring with the most inflammatory symptoms of the disease; nor is it to be wondered at, since the appetite is frequently unimpaired, and the generation of blood continues to be the same as in perfect health.

Dr. Cullen recommends the use of bleeding in consumptions, in order to lessen the inflammation of the ulcers in the lungs, and thereby to dispose them to heal. From the testimonies of the relief which bleeding affords in external ulcers and tumours accompanied by inflammation, I am disposed to expect the same benefit from it in inflamed ulcers and tumours in the lungs: whether, therefore, we adopt Dr. Cullen's theory of consumption, and treat it as a local disease, or assent to the one which I have delivered, repeated bleedings appear to be equally necessary and useful.

I have seen two cases of inflammatory consumption, attended by a hæmorrhage of a quart of blood from the lungs. I agreed at first with the friends of these patients in expecting a rapid termination of their disease in death, but to the joy and surprise of all connected with them, they both recovered. I ascribed their recovery wholly to the inflammatory action of their systems being suddenly reduced by a spontaneous discharge of blood. These facts, I hope, will serve to establish the usefulness of blood-letting in the inflammatory state of consumption, with those physicians who are yet disposed to trust more to the fortuitous operations of nature, than to the decisions of reason and experience.

I have always found this remedy to be more necessary in the winter and first spring months, than at any other season. We obtain by means of repeated bleedings, such a mitigation of all the symptoms as enables the patient to use exercise with advantage as soon as the weather becomes so dry and settled, as to admit of his going abroad every day.

The relief obtained by bleeding, is so certain in this state of consumption, that I often use it as a palliative remedy, where I do not expect it will perform a cure. I was lately made happy in finding, that I am not singular in this practice. Dr. Hamilton, of Lynn Regis, used it with success in a consumption, which was the effect of a most deplorable scrophula, without entertaining the least hope of its performing a cure[26]. In those cases where inflammatory action attends the last scene of the disease, there is often more relief obtained by a little bleeding than by the use of opiates, and it is always a more humane prescription, in desperate cases, than the usual remedies of vomits and blisters.

I once bled a sea captain, whom I had declared to be within a few hours of his dissolution, in order to relieve him of uncommon pain, and difficulty in breathing. His pulse was at the same time hard. The evacuation, though it consisted of but four ounces of blood, had the wished for effect, and his death, I have reason to believe, was rendered more easy by it. The blood, in this case, was covered with a buffy coat.

The quantity of blood drawn in every case of inflammatory consumption, should be determined by the force of the pulse, and the habits of the patient. I have seldom taken more than eight, but more frequently but six ounces at a time. It is much better to repeat the bleeding once or twice a week, than to use it less frequently, but in larger quantities.

From many years experience of the efficacy of bleeding in this state of consumption, I feel myself authorised to assert, that where a greater proportion of persons die of consumption when it makes its first appearance in the lungs, with symptoms of inflammatory diathesis, than die of ordinary pneumonies (provided exercise be used afterwards), it must, in nine cases out of ten, be ascribed to the ignorance, or erroneous theories of physicians, or to the obstinacy or timidity of patients.

In speaking thus confidently of the necessity and benefits of bleeding in the inflammatory state of consumption, I confine myself to observations made chiefly in the state of Pennsylvania. It is possible the inhabitants of European countries and cities, may so far have passed the simple ages of inflammatory diseases, as never to exhibit those symptoms on which I have founded the indication of blood-letting. I suspect moreover that in most of the southern states of America, the inflammatory action of the arterial system is of too transient a nature to admit of the repeated bleedings in the consumption which are used with so much advantage in the middle and northern states.

In reviewing the prejudices against this excellent remedy in consumptions, I have frequently wished to discover such a substitute for it as would with equal safety and certainty take down the morbid excitement, and action of the arterial system. At present we know of no such remedy; and until it be discovered, it becomes us to combat the prejudices against bleeding; and to derive all the advantages from it which have been mentioned.

2. A second remedy for the inflammatory state of consumption should be sought for in a MILK and VEGETABLE DIET. In those cases where the milk does not lie easy on the stomach, it should be mixed with water, or it should be taken without its cheesy or oily parts, as in whey, or butter-milk, or it should be taken without skimming; for there are cases in which milk will agree with the stomach in this state, and in no other. The oil of the milk probably helps to promote the solution of its curds in the stomach. It is seldom in the power of physicians to prescribe ass' or goat's milk in this disease; but a good substitute may be prepared for them by adding to cow's milk a little sugar, and a third or fourth part of water, or of a weak infusion of green tea. The quantity of milk taken in a day should not exceed a pint, and even less than that quantity when we wish to lessen the force of the pulse by the abstraction of nourishment. The vegetables which are eaten in this state of the disease, should contain as little stimulus as possible. Rice, in all the ways in which it is usually prepared for aliment, should be preferred to other grains, and the less saccharine fruits to those which abound with sugar. In those cases where the stomach is disposed to dyspepsia, a little salted meat, fish, or oysters, also soft boiled eggs, may be taken with safety, mixed with vegetable aliment. Where there is no morbid affection of the stomach, I have seen the white meats eaten without increasing the inflammatory symptoms of the disease. The transition from a full diet to milk and vegetables should be gradual, and the addition of animal to vegetable aliment, should be made with the same caution. From the neglect of this direction, much error, both in theory and practice, has arisen in the treatment of consumptions.

In every case it will be better for the patient to eat four or five, rather than but two or three meals in a day. A less stimulus is by this means communicated to the system, and less chyle is mixed with the blood in a given time. Of so much importance do I conceive this direction to be, that I seldom prescribe for a chronic disease of any kind without enforcing it.

3. VOMITS have been much commended by Dr. Read in this disease. From their indiscriminate use in every state of consumption, I believe they have oftener done harm than good. In cases where a patient objects to bleeding, or where a physician doubts of its propriety, vomits may always be substituted in its room with great advantage. They are said to do most service when the disease is the effect of a catarrh.

4. NITRE, in moderate doses of ten or fifteen grains, taken three or four times a day, has sometimes been useful in this disease; but it has been only when the disease has appeared with inflammatory symptoms. Care should be taken not to persevere too long in the use of this remedy, as it is apt to impair the appetite. I have known one case in which it produced an obstinate dyspepsia, and a disposition to the colic; but it removed, at the same time, the symptoms of pulmonary consumption.

5. COLD and DRY AIR, when combined with the exercise of *walking*, deserves to be mentioned as an antiphlogistic remedy. I have repeatedly prescribed it in this species of the consumption with advantage, and have often had the pleasure of finding a single walk of two or three miles in a clear cold day, produce nearly the same diminution of the force and frequency of the pulse, as the loss of six or eight ounces of blood.

I come now to treat of the palliative remedies which are proper in the

II. Or HECTIC STATE of consumption. Here we begin to behold the disease in a new and more distressing form than in the state which has been described. There is in this state of consumption the same complication of inflammatory and typhus diathesis which occurs in the typhoid and puerperile fevers, and of course the same difficulty in treating it successfully; for the same remedies do good and harm, according as the former or latter diathesis prevails in the system.

All that I shall say upon this state is, that the treatment of it should be accommodated to the predominance of inflammatory or typhus symptoms, for the hectic state presents each of them alternately every week, and sometimes every day to the hand, or eye of a physician. When a hard pulse with acute pains in the side and breast occur, bleeding and other remedies for the inflammatory state must be used; but when the disease exhibits a predominance of typhus symptoms, the remedies for that state to be mentioned immediately, should be prescribed in moderate doses. There are several palliative medicines which have been found useful in the hectic state, but they are such as belong alike to the other two states; and therefore will be mentioned hereafter in a place assigned to them.

I am sorry, however, to add, that where bleeding has not been indicated, I have seldom been able to afford much relief by medicine in this state of consumption. I have used alternately the most gentle, and the most powerful vegetable and metallic tonics to no purpose. Even arsenic has failed in my hands of affording the least alleviation of the hectic fever. I conceive the removal of this fever to be the great desideratum in the cure of consumption; and should it be found, after all our researches, to exist only in exercise, it will be no departure from a law of nature, for I believe there are no diseases produced by equal degrees of chronic debility, in which medicines are of any more efficacy, than they are in the hectic fever of the pulmonary consumption.

I proceed now to speak of the palliative remedies which are proper in the

III. Or TYPHUS STATE of the pulmonary consumption.

The first of these are STIMULATING MEDICINES. However just the complaints of Dr. Fothergill may be against the use of balsams in the inflammatory and mixed states of consumption, they appear to be not only safe, but useful likewise, in mitigating the symptoms of weak morbid action in the arterial system. I have therefore frequently prescribed opium, the balsam of copaivæ, of Peru, the oil of amber, and different preparations of turpentine and tar, in moderate doses, with obvious advantage. Garlic, elixir of vitriol, the juice of dandelion, a strong tea made of horehound, and a decoction of the inner bark of the wild cherry tree[27], also bitters of all kinds, have all been found safe and useful tonics in this state of consumption. Even the Peruvian bark and the cold bath, so often and so generally condemned in consumptions, are always innocent, and frequently active remedies, where there is a total absence of inflammatory diathesis in this disease. The bark is said to be most useful when the consumption is the consequence of an intermitting fever, and when it occurs in old people. With these remedies should be combined

2. A CORDIAL and STIMULATING DIET. Milk and vegetables, so proper in the inflammatory, are improper, when taken alone, in this state of consumption. I believe they often accelerate that decay of appetite and diarrhœa, which form the closing scene of the disease. I have lately seen three persons recovered from the lowest stage of this state of consumption, by the use of animal food and cordial drinks, aided by frequent doses of opium, taken during the day as well as in the night. I should hesitate in mentioning these cures, had they not been witnessed by more than a hundred students

of medicine in the Pennsylvania hospital. The history of one of them is recorded in the 5th volume of the New-York Medical Repository, and of the two others in Dr. Coxe's Medical Museum. Oysters, it has been said, have performed cures of consumption. If they have, it must have been only when they were eaten in that state of it which is now under consideration. They are a most savoury and wholesome article of diet, in all diseases of weak morbid action. To the cordial articles of diet belong sweet vegetable matters. Grapes, sweet apples, and the juice of the sugar maple tree, when taken in large quantities, have all cured this disease. They all appear to act by filling the blood-vessels, and thereby imparting tone to the whole system. I have found the same advantage from dividing the meals in this state of consumption, that I mentioned under a former head. The exhibition of food in this case, should not be left to the calls of appetite, any more than the exhibition of a medicine. Indeed food may be made to supply the place of cordial medicines, by keeping up a constant and gentle action in the whole system. For this reason, I have frequently advised my patients never to suffer their stomachs to be empty, even for a single hour. I have sometimes aimed to keep up the influence of a gentle action in the stomach upon the whole system, by advising them to eat in the night, in order to obviate the increase of secretion into the lungs and of the cough in the morning, which are brought on in part by the increase of debility from the long abstraction of the stimulus of aliment during the night.

However safe, and even useful, the cordial medicines and diet that have been mentioned may appear, yet I am sorry to add, that we seldom see any other advantages from them than a mitigation of distressing symptoms, except when they have been followed by suitable and long continued exercise. Even under this favourable circumstance, they are often ineffectual; for there frequently occurs, in this state of consumption, such a destruction of the substance and functions of the lungs, as to preclude the possibility of a recovery by the use of any of the remedies which have been discovered. Perhaps, where this is not the case, their want of efficacy may be occasioned by their being given before the pulse is completely reduced to a typhus state. The weaker the pulse, the greater is the probability of benefit being derived from the use of cordial diet and medicines.

I have said formerly, that the three states of consumption do not observe any regular course in succeeding each other. They are not only complicated in some instances, but they often appear and disappear half a dozen times in the course of the disease, according to the influence of the weather, dress, diet, and the passions upon the system. The great secret, therefore, of treating this disease consists in accommodating all the remedies that have been mentioned to the predominance of any of the three different states of the system, as manifested chiefly by the pulse. It is in consequence of having observed the evils which have resulted from the ignorance or neglect of this practice, that I have sometimes wished that it were possible to abolish the seducing nomenclature of diseases altogether, in order thereby to oblige physicians to conform exactly to the fluctuating state of the system in all their prescriptions; for it is not more certain, that, in all cultivated languages, every idea has its appropriate word, than that every state of a disease has its appropriate dose of medicine, the knowledge and application of which can alone constitute rational, or secure uniformly successful practice.

I come now to say a few words upon those palliative remedies which are alike proper in every state of the pulmonary consumption.

The first remedy under this head is a DRY SITUATION. A damp air, whether breathed in a room, or out of doors, is generally hurtful in every form of this disease. A kitchen, or a bed-room, below the level of the ground, has often produced, and never fails to increase, a pulmonary consumption. I have often observed a peculiar paleness (the first symptom of general debility) to show itself very early in the faces of persons who work or sleep in cellar kitchens or shops.

2. COUNTRY AIR. The higher and drier the situation which is chosen for the purpose of enjoying the benefit of this remedy, the better. Situations exposed to the sea, should be carefully avoided; for it is a singular fact, that while consumptive persons are benefited by the sea-air, when they breathe it on the ocean, they are always injured by that portion of it which they breathe on the sea-shore. To show its influence, not only in aggravating consumptions, but in disposing to them, and in adding to the mortality of another disease of the lungs, I shall subjoin the following facts. From one fourth to one half of all the adults who die in Great Britain, Dr. Willan says, perish with this disease. In Salem, in the state of Massachusetts, which is situated near the sea, and exposed, during many months in the year, to a moist east wind, there died, in the year 1799, one hundred and sixty persons, fifty-three died of the consumption, making in all nearly one third of all the inhabitants of the town. Eight more died of what is called a lung fever, probably of what is called in Pennsylvania the galloping grade of that disease. Consumptions are more frequent in Boston, Rhode-Island, and New-York, from their damp winds, and vicinity to the sea-shore, than they are in Philadelphia. In the neighbourhood of Cape May, which lies near the sea-shore of New-Jersey, there are three religious societies, among whom the influenza prevailed in the year 1790. Its mortality, under equal circumstances, was in the exact ratio to their vicinity to the sea. The deaths were most numerous in that society which was nearest to it, and least so in that which was most remote from it. These unfriendly effects of the sea air, in the above pulmonary diseases, do not appear to be produced simply by its moisture. Consumptions are scarcely known in the moist atmosphere which so

generally prevails in Lincolnshire, in England, and in the inland parts of Holland and Ireland.

I shall not pause to inquire, why a mixture of land and sea air is so hurtful in the consumption, and at the same time so agreeable to persons in health, and so medicinal in many other diseases, but shall dismiss this head by adding a fact which was communicated to me by Dr. Matthew Irvine, of South-Carolina, and that is, That those situations which are in the neighbourhood of bays or rivers, where the salt and fresh waters mix their streams together, are more unfavourable to consumptive patients than the sea-shore, and therefore should be more carefully avoided by them in exchanging city for country air.

3. A CHANGE OF CLIMATE. It is remarkable that climates uniformly cold or warm, which seldom produce consumptions, are generally fatal to persons who visit them in that disease. Countries between the 30th and 40th degrees of latitude are most friendly to consumptive people.

4. LOOSE DRESSES, AND A CAREFUL ACCOMMODATION OF THEM TO THE CHANGES IN THE WEATHER. Many facts might be mentioned to show the influence of compression and of tight ligatures of every kind, upon the different parts of the body; also of too much, or too little clothing, in producing, or increasing diseases of every kind, more especially those which affect the lungs. Tight stays, garters, waistbands, and collars, should all be laid aside in the consumption, and the quality of the clothing should be suited to the weather. A citizen of Maryland informed me, that he twice had a return of a cough and spitting of blood, by wearing his summer clothes a week after the weather became cool in the month of September. But it is not sufficient to vary the weight or quality of dress with the seasons. It should be varied with the changes which take place in the temperature of the air every day, even in the summer months, in middle latitudes. I know a citizen of Philadelphia, who has laboured under a consumptive diathesis near thirty years, who believes that he has lessened the frequency and violence of pulmonic complaints during that time, by a careful accommodation of his dress to the weather. He has been observed frequently to change his waistcoat and small clothes twice or three times in a day, in a summer month.

A repetition of colds, and thereby an increase of the disease, will be prevented by wearing flannel next to the skin in winter, and muslin in the summer, either in the form of a shirt or a waistcoat: where these are objected to, a piece of flannel, or of soft sheepskin, should be worn next to the breast.

They not only prevent colds, but frequently remove chronic pains from that part of the body.

5. ARTIFICIAL EVACUATIONS, by means of BLISTERS and ISSUES. I suspect the usefulness of these remedies to be chiefly confined to the inflammatory and hectic states of consumption. In the typhus state, the system is too weak to sustain the discharges of either of them. Fresh blisters should be preferred to such as are perpetual, and the issues, to be useful, should be large. They are supposed to afford relief by diverting a preternatural secretion and excretion of mucus or pus from the lungs, to an artificial emunctory in a less vital part of the body. Blisters do most service when the disease arises from repelled eruptions, and when they are applied between the shoulders, and the upper and internal parts of the arms. When it arises from rheumatism and gout, the blisters should be applied to the joints, and such other external parts of the body as had been previously affected by those diseases.

6. Certain FUMIGATIONS and VAPOURS. An accidental cure of a pulmonary affection by the smoke of rosin, in a man who bottled liquors, raised for a while the credit of fumigations. I have tried them, but without much permanent effect. I think I have seen the pain in the breast relieved by receiving the vapour from a mixture of equal parts of tar, bran, and boiling water into the lungs. The sulphureous and saline air of Stabiæ, between Mount Vesuvius and the Mediterranean Sea, and the effluvia of the pine forests of Lybia, were supposed, in ancient times, to be powerful remedies in consumptive complaints; but it is probable, the exercise used in travelling to those countries, contributed chiefly to the cures which were ascribed to foreign matters acting upon the lungs.

7. LOZENGES, SYRUPS, and DEMULCENT TEAS. These are too common and too numerous to be mentioned.

8. OPIATES. It is a mistake in practice, founded upon a partial knowledge of the qualities of opium, to administer it only at night, or to suppose that its effects in composing a cough depend upon its inducing sleep. It should be given in small doses during the day, as well as in larger ones at night. The dose should be proportioned to the degrees of action in the arterial system. The less this action, the more opium may be taken with safety and advantage.

9. DIFFERENT POSITIONS OF THE BODY have been found to be more or less favourable to the abatement of the cough. These positions should be carefully sought for, and the body kept in that which procures the most freedom from coughing. I have heard of an instance in which a cough, which threatened a return of the hæmorrhage from the lungs, was perfectly composed for two weeks, by keeping the patient nearly in one posture in bed;

but I have known more cases in which relief from coughing was to be obtained only by an erect posture of the body.

10. Considerable relief will often be obtained from the patient's SLEEPING BETWEEN BLANKETS in winter, and on a MATTRASS[** sic] in summer. The former prevent fresh cold from night sweats; the latter frequently checks them altogether. In cases where a sufficient weight of blankets to keep up an agreeable warmth cannot be borne, without restraining easy and full acts of inspiration, the patient should sleep under a light feather bed, or an eider down coverlet. They both afford more warmth than double or treble their weight of blankets.

However comfortable this mode of producing warmth in bed may be, it does not protect the lungs from the morbid effects of the distant points of temperature of a warm parlour in the day time, and a cold bed-chamber at night. To produce an equable temperature of air at all hours, I have frequently advised my patients, when going to a warm climate was not practicable, to pass their nights as well as days in an open stove room, in which nearly the same degrees of heat were kept up at all hours. I have found this practice, in several cases, a tolerable substitute for a warm climate.

11. The MODERATE use of the lungs, in READING, PUBLIC SPEAKING, LAUGHING, and SINGING. The lungs, when debilitated, derive equal benefit with the limbs, or other parts of the body, from moderate exercise. I have mentioned, in another place[28], several facts which support this opinion. But too much pains cannot be taken to inculcate upon our patients to avoid all *excess* in the use of the lungs, by *long*, or *loud* reading, speaking, or singing, or by sudden and violent *bursts* of laughter. I shall long lament the death of a female patient, who had discovered many hopeful signs of a recovery from a consumption, who relapsed, and died, in consequence of bursting a blood-vessel in her lungs, by a sudden fit of laughter.

12. Are there any advantages to be derived from the excitement of certain PASSIONS in the treatment of consumptions? Dr. Blane tells us, that many consumptive persons were relieved, and that some recovered, in consequence of the terror which was excited by a hurricane in Barbadoes, in the year 1780. It will be difficult to imitate, by artificial means, the accidental cures which are recorded by Dr. Blane; but we learn enough from them to inspire the invigorating passions of hope and confidence in the minds of our patients, and to recommend to them such exercises as produce exertions of body and mind analogous to those which are produced by terror. Van Sweiten and Smollet relate cures of consumptions, by patients falling into streams of cold water. Perhaps, in both instances, the cures were performed only by the fright and consequent exertion produced by the fall. This is only one instance out of many which might be mentioned, of partial and unequal

action being suddenly changed into general and equal excitement in every part of the system. The cures of consumptions which have been performed by a camp life[29], have probably been much assisted by the commotions in the passions which were excited by the various and changing events of war.

13. A SALIVATION has lately been prescribed in this disease with success. An accident first suggested its advantages, in the Pennsylvania hospital, in the year 1800[30]. Since that time, it has performed many cures in different parts of the United States. It is to be lamented, that in a majority of the cases in which the mercury has been given, it has failed of exciting a salivation. Where it affects the mouth, it generally succeeds in recent cases, which is more than can be said of any, or of all other remedies in this disease. In its hectic state, a salivation frequently cures, and even in its typhus and last stage, I have more than once prescribed it with success. The same regard to the pulse should regulate the use of this new remedy in consumption, that has been recommended in other febrile diseases. It should never be advised until the inflammatory diathesis of the system has been in a great degree reduced, by the depleting remedies formerly mentioned.

During the use of the above remedies, great care should be taken to relieve the patient from the influence of all those debilitating and irritating causes which induced the disease. I shall say elsewhere that decayed teeth are one of them. These should be extracted where there is reason to suspect they have produced, or that they increase the disease.

I have hitherto said nothing of the digitalis as a palliative remedy in pulmonary consumption. I am sorry to acknowledge that, in many cases in which I have prescribed it, it has done no good, and in some it has done harm. From the opposite accounts of physicians of the most respectable characters of the effects of this medicine, I have been inclined to ascribe its different issues, to a difference in the soil in which it has been cultivated, or in the times of gathering, or in the manner of preparing it, all of which we know influence the qualities of many other vegetables. If the theory of consumption which I have endeavoured to establish be admitted, that uncertain and unsafe medicine will be rendered unnecessary by the remedies that have been enumerated, provided they are administered at the times, and in the manner that has been recommended.

Before I proceed to speak of the radical cure of the consumption, it will be necessary to observe, that by means of the palliative remedies which have been mentioned, many persons have been recovered, and some have had their lives prolonged by them for many years; but in most of these cases I have found, upon inquiry, that the disease recurred as soon as the patient left off the use of his remedies, unless they were followed by necessary or voluntary exercise.

It is truly surprising to observe how long some persons have lived who have been affected by a consumptive diathesis, and by frequent attacks of many of the most troublesome symptoms of this disease. Van Sweiten mentions the case of a man, who had lived thirty years in this state. Morton relates the history of a man, in whom the symptoms of consumption appeared with but little variation or abatement from his early youth till the 70th year of his age. The widow of the celebrated Senac lived to be 84 years of age, thirty of which she passed in a pulmonary consumption. Dr. Nicols was subject to occasional attacks of this disease during his whole life, and he lived to be above eighty years of age. Bennet says he knew an instance in which it continued above sixty years. I prescribed for my first pupil, Dr. Edwards, in a consumption in the year 1769. He lived until 1802, and seldom passed a year without spitting blood, nor a week without a cough, during that long interval of time. The fatal tendency of his disease was constantly opposed by occasional blood-letting, rural exercises, a cordial, but temperate diet, the Peruvian bark, two sea voyages, and travelling in foreign countries. There are besides these instances of long protracted consumptions, cases of it which appear in childhood, and continue for many years. I have seldom known them prove fatal under puberty.

I am led here to mention another instance of the analogy between pneumony and the pulmonary consumption. We often see the same frequency of recurrence of both diseases in habits which are predisposed to them. I have attended a German citizen of Philadelphia, in several fits of the pneumony, who has been confined to his bed eight-and-twenty times, by the same disease, in the course of the same number of years. He has, for the most part, enjoyed good health in the intervals of those attacks, and always appeared, till lately, to possess a good constitution. In the cases of the frequent recurrence of pneumony, no one has suspected the disease to have originated exclusively in a morbid state of the lungs; on the contrary, it appears evidently to be produced by the *sudden* influence of the same causes, which, by acting with less force, and for a *longer* time, produce the pulmonary consumption. The name of pneumony is taken from the principal symptom of this disease, but it as certainly belongs to the whole arterial system as the consumption; and I add further, that it is as certainly produced by general predisposing debility. The hardness and fulness of the pulse do not militate against this assertion, for they are altogether the effects of a morbid and convulsive excitement of the sanguiferous system. The strength manifested by the pulse is moreover partial, for every other part of the body discovers, at the same time, signs of extreme debility.

It would be easy, by pursuing this subject a little further, to mention a number of facts which, by the aid of principles in physiology and pathology, which are universally admitted, would open to us a new theory of fevers, but this would lead us too far from the subject before us. I shall only remark, that all that has been said of the influence of *general* debilitating causes upon the lungs, both in pneumony and consumption, and of the alternation of the consumption with other general diseases, will receive great support from considering the lungs only as a part of the whole external surface of the body, upon which most of the remote and exciting causes of both diseases produce their first effects. This extent of the surface of the body, not only to the lungs, but to the alimentary canal, was first taken notice of by Dr. Boerhaave; but was unhappily neglected by him in his theories of the diseases of the lungs and bowels. Dr. Keil supposes that the lungs, from the peculiar structure of the bronchial vessels, and air vesicles, expose a surface to the action of the air, equal to the extent of the whole external and visible surface of the body.

Thus have I mentioned the usual palliative remedies for the consumption. Many of these remedies, under certain circumstances, I have said have cured the disease, but I suspect that most of these cures have taken place only when the disease has partaken of an intermediate nature between a pneumony and a true pulmonary consumption. Such connecting shades, appear between the extreme points of many other diseases. In a former essay[31], I endeavoured to account for the transmutation (if I may be allowed the expression) of the pneumony into the consumption, by ascribing it to the increase of the debilitating refinements of civilized life. This opinion has derived constant support from every observation I have made connected with this subject, since its first publication, in the year 1772.

I come now to treat of the RADICAL REMEDIES for the pulmonary consumption.

In an essay formerly alluded to[32], I mentioned the effects of labour, and the hardships of a camp or naval life, upon this disease. As there must frequently occur such objections to each of those remedies, as to forbid their being recommended or adopted, it will be necessary to seek for substitutes for them in the different species of exercise. These are, *active*, *passive*, and *mixed*. The *active* includes walking, and the exercise of the hands and feet in working or dancing. The *passive* includes rocking in a cradle, swinging, sailing, and riding in carriages of different kinds. The *mixed* is confined chiefly to riding on horseback.

I have mentioned all the different species of exercise, not because I think they all belong to the class of radical remedies for the consumption, but because it is often necessary to use those which are passive, before we recommend those of a mixed or active nature. That physician does not err more who advises a patient to take physic, without specifying its qualities and doses, than the physician does who advises a patient, in a consumption, to use exercise, without specifying its species and degrees. From the neglect of this direction, we often find consumptive patients injured instead of being relieved by exercises, which, if used with judgment, might have been attended with the happiest effects.

I have before suggested that the stimulus of every medicine, which is intended to excite action in the system, should always be in an exact ratio to its excitability. The same rule should be applied to the stimulus of exercise. I have heard a well-attested case of a young lady, upon whose consumption the first salutary impression was made by rocking her in a cradle; and I know another case in which a young lady, in the lowest state of that debility which precedes an affection of the lungs, was prepared for the use of the mixed and active exercises, by being first moved gently backwards and forwards in a chariot without horses, for an hour every day. Swinging appears to act in the same gentle manner. In the case of a gardener, who was far advanced in a consumption, in the Pennsylvania hospital, I had the pleasure of observing its good effects, in an eminent degree. It so far restored him, as to enable him to complete his recovery by working at his former occupation.

In cases of extreme debility, the following order should be recommended in the use of the different species of exercise.

1. Rocking in a cradle, or riding on an elastic board, commonly called a chamber-horse.

2. Swinging.

3. Sailing.

4. Riding in a carriage.

5. Riding on horseback.

6. Walking.

7. Running and dancing.

In the use of each of those species of exercise great attention should be paid to the *degree* or *force* of action with which they are applied to the body. For example, in riding in a carriage, the exercise will be less in a four-wheel carriage than in a single horse chair, and less when the horses move in a walking, than a trotting gait. In riding on horseback, the exercise will be less or greater according as the horse walks, paces, canters, or trots, in passing over the ground.

I have good reason to believe, that an English sea-captain, who was on the verge of the grave with the consumption, in the spring of the year 1790, owed his perfect recovery to nothing but the above gradual manner, in which, by my advice, he made use of the exercises of riding in a carriage and on horseback. I have seen many other cases of the good effects of thus accommodating exercise to debility; and I am sorry to add, that I have seen many cases in which, from the neglect of this manner of using exercise, most of the species and degrees of it, have either been useless, or done harm. However carelessly this observation may be read by physicians, or attended to by patients, I conceive no direction to be more necessary in the cure of consumptions. I have been thus particular in detailing it, not only because I believe it to be important, but that I might atone to society for that portion of evil which I might have prevented by a more strict attention to it in the first years of my practice.

The more the arms are used in exercise the better. One of the proprietary governors of Pennsylvania, who laboured for many years under consumptive diathesis, derived great benefit from frequently rowing himself in a small boat, a few miles up and down the river Schuylkill. Two young men, who were predisposed to a consumption, were perfectly cured by working steadily at a printing press in this city. A French physician in Martinique cured this disease, by simply rubbing the arms between the shoulders and the elbows, until they inflamed. The remedy is strongly recommended, by the recoveries from pulmonary consumption which have followed abscesses in the arm-pits. Perhaps the superior advantages of riding on horseback, in this disease, may arise in part from the constant and gentle use of the arms in the management of the bridle and the whip.

Much has been said in favour of sea voyages in consumptions. In the mild degrees of the disease they certainly have done service, but I suspect the relief given, or the cures performed by them, should be confined chiefly to seafaring people, who add to the benefits of a constant change of pure air, a share of the invigorating exercises of navigating the ship. I have frequently heard of consumptive patients reviving at sea, probably from the transient effects of sea sickness upon the whole system, and growing worse as soon as they came near the end of their voyage. It would seem as if the mixture of land and sea airs was hurtful to the lungs, in every situation and condition in which it could be applied to them. Nor are the peculiar and morbid effects of the first operation of land and sea airs upon the human body, in sea voyages, confined only to consumptive people. I crossed the Atlantic ocean, in the year 1766, with a sea captain, who announced to his passengers the agreeable news that we were near the British coast, before any discovery had been made of our situation by sounding, or by a change in the colour of the water. Upon asking him upon what he founded his opinion, he said, that he had been sneezing, which, he added, was the sign of an approaching cold, and that, in the course of upwards of twenty years, he had never made the land (to use the seaman's phrase) without being affected in a similar manner.

I have visited many sick people in Philadelphia, soon after their arrival from sea, who have informed me, that they had enjoyed good health during the greatest part of their voyage, and that they had contracted their indispositions after they came within sight of the land. I mention these facts only to show the necessity of advising consumptive patients, who undertake a sea voyage for the recovery of their health, not to expose themselves upon deck in the morning and at night, after they arrive within the region in which the mixture of the land and sea airs may be supposed to take place.

I subscribe, from what I have observed, to the bold declaration of Dr. Sydenham, in favour of the efficacy of riding on horseback, in the cure of consumption. I do not think the existence of an abscess, when broken, or even tubercles in the lungs, when recent, or of a moderate size, the least objection to the use of this excellent remedy. An abscess in the lungs is not necessarily fatal, and tubercles have no malignity in them which should render their removal impracticable by this species of exercise. The first question, therefore, to be asked by a physician who visits a patient in this disease should be, not what is the state of his lungs, but, is he able to ride on horseback.

There are two methods of riding for health in this disease. The first is by short excursions; the second is by long journies. In slight consumptive affections, and after a recovery from an acute illness, short excursions are sufficient to remove the existing debility; but in the more advanced stages of consumption, they are seldom effectual, and frequently do harm, by exciting an occasional appetite without adding to the digestive powers. They, moreover, keep the system constantly vibrating by their unavoidable inconstancy, between distant points of tone and debility[33], and they are unhappily accompanied at all times, from the want of a succession of fresh objects to divert the mind, by the melancholy reflection that they are the sad, but necessary conditions of life.

In a consumption of long continuance or of great danger, long journies on horseback are the most effectual modes of exercise. They afford a constant succession of fresh objects and company, which divert the mind from dwelling upon the danger of the existing malady; they are moreover attended by a constant change of air, and they are not liable to be interrupted by company, or transient changes in the weather, by which means appetite and digestion, action and power, all keep pace with each other. It is to be lamented that the use of this excellent remedy is frequently opposed by indolence and narrow circumstances in both sexes, and by the peculiarity of situation and temper in the female sex. Women are attached to their families by stronger ties than men. They cannot travel alone. Their delicacy, which is increased by sickness, is liable to be offended at every stage; and, lastly, they sooner relax in their exertions to prolong their lives than men. Of the truth of the last observation, sir William Hamilton has furnished us with a striking illustration. He tells us, that in digging into the ruins produced by the late earthquake in Calabria, the women who perished in it, were all found with their arms folded, as if they had abandoned themselves immediately to despair and death; whereas, the men were found with their arms extended, as if they had resisted their fate to the last moment of their lives. It would seem, from this fact, and many others of a similar nature which might be related, that a capacity of bearing pain and distress with fortitude and resignation, was the distinguishing characteristic of the female mind; while a disposition to resist and overcome evil, belonged in a more peculiar manner to the mind of man. I have mentioned this peculiarity of circumstances and temper in female patients, only for the sake of convincing physicians that it will be necessary for them to add all the force of eloquence to their advice, when they recommend journies to women in preference to all other remedies, for the recovery of their health.

Persons, moreover, who pursue active employments, frequently object to undertaking journies, from an opinion that their daily occupations are sufficient to produce all the salutary effects we expect from artificial exercise. It will be highly necessary to correct this mistake, by assuring such persons that, however useful the habitual exercise of an active, or even a laborious employment may be to *preserve* health, it must always be exchanged for one which excites new impressions, both upon the mind and body, in every attempt to *restore* the system from that debility which is connected with pulmonary consumption.

As travelling is often rendered useless, and even hurtful in this disease, from being pursued in an improper manner, it will be necessary to furnish our patients with such directions as will enable them to derive the greatest benefit from their journies. I shall, therefore, in this place, mention the substance of the directions which I have given in writing for many years to such consumptive patients as undertake journies by my advice.

1. To avoid fatigue. Too much cannot be said to enforce this direction. It is the hinge on which the recovery or death of a consumptive patient frequently turns. I repeat it again, therefore, that patients should be charged over and over when they set off on a journey, as well as when they use exercise of any kind, to avoid fatigue. For this purpose they should begin by travelling only a few miles in a day, and increase the distance of their stages, as they increase their strength. By neglecting this practice, many persons have returned from journies much worse than when they left home, and many have died in taverns, or at the houses of their friends on the road. Travelling in stage-coaches is seldom safe for a consumptive patient. They are often

crowded; they give too much motion; and they afford by their short delays and distant stages, too little time for rest, or for taking the frequent refreshment which was formerly recommended.

2. To avoid travelling too soon in the morning, and after the going down of the sun in the evening, and, if the weather be hot, never to travel in the middle of the day. The sooner a patient breakfasts after he leaves his bed the better; and in no case should he leave his morning stage with an empty stomach.

3. If it should be necessary for a patient to lie down, or to sleep in the day time, he should be advised to undress himself, and to cover his body between sheets or blankets. The usual ligatures of garters, stocks, knee-bands, waistcoats, and shoes, are very unfriendly to sound sleep; hence persons who lie down with their clothes on, often awake from an afternoon's nap in terror from dreams, or in a profuse sweat, or with a head-ach or sick stomach; and generally out of humour. The surveyors are so sensible of the truth of this remark, that they always undress themselves when they sleep in the woods. An intelligent gentleman of this profession informed me, that he had frequently seen young woodsmen, who had refused to conform to this practice, so much indisposed in the morning, that, after the experience of a few nights, they were forced to adopt it.

Great care should be taken in sleeping, whether in the day time or at night, never to lie down in damp sheets. Dr. Sydenham excepts the danger from this quarter, when he speaks of the efficacy of travelling on horseback in curing the consumption.

4. Patients who travel for health in this disease should avoid all large companies, more especially evening and night parties. The air of a contaminated room, phlogisticated by the breath of fifteen or twenty persons, and by the same number of burning candles, is poison to a consumptive patient. To avoid impure air from every other source, he should likewise avoid sleeping in a crowded room, or with curtains around his bed, and even with a bed-fellow.

5. Travelling, to be effectual in this disease, should be conducted in such a manner as that a patient may escape the extremes of heat and cold. For this purpose he should pass the winter, and part of the spring, in Georgia or South-Carolina, and the summer in New-Hampshire, Massachusetts, or Vermont, or, if he pleases, he may still more effectually shun the summer heats, by crossing the lakes, and travelling along the shores of the St. Laurence to the city of Quebec. He will thus escape the extremes of heat and cold, particularly the less avoidable one of heat; for I have constantly found the hot month of July to be as unfriendly to consumptive patients in Pennsylvania, as the variable month of March. By these means too he will

enjoy nearly an equable temperature of air in every month of the year; and his system will be free from the inconvenience of the alternate action of heat and cold upon it. The autumnal months should be spent in New-Jersey or Pennsylvania.

In these journies from north to south, or from south to north, he should be careful, for reasons before mentioned, to keep at as great a distance as possible from the sea coast. Should this inquiry fall into the hands of a British physician, I would beg leave to suggest to him, whether more advantages would not accrue to his consumptive patients from advising them to cross the Atlantic ocean, and afterwards to pursue the tour which I have recommended, than by sending them to Portugal, France, or Italy. Here they will arrive with such a mitigation of the violence of the disease, in consequence of the length of their sea voyage, as will enable them immediately to begin their journies on horseback. Here they will be exposed to fewer temptations to intemperance, or to unhealthy amusements, than in old European countries. And, lastly, in the whole course of this tour, they will travel among a people related to them by a sameness of language and manners, and by ancient or modern ties of citizenship. Long journies for the recovery of health, under circumstances so agreeable, should certainly be preferred to travelling among strangers of different nations, languages, and manners, on the continent of Europe.

6. To render travelling on horseback effectual in a consumption, it should be continued with moderate intervals from *six to twelve months*. But the cure should not be rested upon a single journey. It should be repeated every *two* or *three years*, till our patient has passed the consumptive stages of life. Nay, he must do more; he must acquire a *habit* of riding constantly, both at home and abroad; or, to use the words of Dr. Fuller, "he must, like a Tartar, learn to live on horseback, by which means he will acquire in time the constitution of a Tartar[34]."

Where benefit is expected from a change of climate, as well as from travelling, patients should reside at least two years in the place which is chosen for that purpose. I have seldom known a residence for a shorter time in a foreign climate do much service.

To secure a perfect obedience to medical advice, it would be extremely useful if consumptive patients could always be accompanied by a physician. Celsus says, he found it more easy to cure the dropsy in slaves than in freemen, because they more readily submitted to the restraints he imposed upon their appetites. Madness has become a curable disease in England, since the physicians of that country have opened private mad-houses, and have taken the entire and constant direction of their patients into their own hands.

The same successful practice would probably follow the treatment of consumptions, if patients were constantly kept under the eye and authority of their physicians. The keenness of appetite, and great stock of animal spirits, which those persons frequently possess, hurry them into many excesses which defeat the best concerted plans of a recovery; or, if they escape these irregularities, they are frequently seduced from our directions by every quack remedy which is recommended to them. Unfortunately the cough becomes a signal of their disease, at every stage of their journey, and the easy or pleasant prescriptions of even hostlers and ferrymen, are often substituted to the self-denial and exertion which have been imposed by physicians. The love of life in these cases seems to level all capacities; for I have observed persons of the most cultivated understandings to yield in common with the vulgar, to the use of these prescriptions.

In a former volume I mentioned the good effects of accidental LABOUR in pulmonary consumptions. The reader will find a particular account in the first volume of Dr. Coxe's Medical Museum, of a clergyman and his wife, in Virginia, being cured by the voluntary use of that remedy.

The following circumstances and symptoms, indicate the longer or shorter duration of this disease, and its issue in life and death:

The consumption from gout, rheumatism, and scrophula, is generally of long duration. It is more rapid in its progress to death, when it arises from a half cured pleurisy, or neglected colds, measles, and influenza. It is of shorter duration in persons under thirty, than in those who are more advanced in life.

It is always dangerous in proportion to the length of time, in which the debilitating causes, that predisposed to it, have acted upon the body.

It is more dangerous when a predisposition to it has been derived from ancestors, than when it has been acquired.

It is generally fatal when accompanied with a bad conformation of the breast.

Chilly fits occurring in the forenoon, are more favourable than when they occur in the evening. They indicate the disease to partake a little of the nature of an intermittent, and are a call for the use of the remedies proper in that disease.

Rheumatic pains, attended with an abatement of the cough, or pains in the breast, are always favourable; so are

Eruptions, or an abscess on the external parts of the body, if they occur before the last stage of the disease.

A spitting of blood, in the early, or forming stage of the disease, is favourable, but after the lungs become much obstructed, or ulcerated, it is most commonly fatal.

A pleurisy, occurring in the low state of the disease, generally kills, but I have seen a case in which it suddenly removed the cough and hectic fever, and thus became the means of prolonging the patient's life for several years.

The discharge of calculi from the lungs by coughing and spitting, and of a thin watery liquid, with a small portion of pus swimming on its surface, are commonly signs of an incurable consumption.

No prediction unfavourable to life can be drawn from pus being discharged from the lungs. We see many recoveries after it has taken place, and many deaths where that symptom has been absent. Large quantities of pus are discharged in consumptions attended with abscesses, and yet few die of them, where they have not been preceded by long continued debility of the whole system. No pus is expectorated from tubercles, and how generally fatal is the disease, after they are formed in the lungs! It is only after they ulcerate that they discharge pus, and it is only after ulcers are thus formed, that the consumption probably becomes uniformly fatal. I suspect these ulcers are sometimes of a cancerous nature.

A sudden cessation of the cough, without a supervening diarrhœa, indicates death to be at hand.

A constant vomiting in a consumption, is generally a bad sign.

Feet obstinately cold, also a swelling of the feet during the day, and of the face in the night, commonly indicate a speedy and fatal issue of the disease.

Lice, and the falling off of the hair, often precede death.

A hoarseness, in the beginning of the disease, is always alarming, but it is more so in its last stage.

A change of the eyes from a blue, or dark, to a light colour, similar to that which takes place in very old people, is a sign of speedy dissolution.

I have never seen a recovery after an apthous sore throat took place.

Death from the consumption comes on in some or more than one, of the following ways:

1. With a diarrhœa. In its absence,

2. With wasting night sweats.

3. A rupture of an abscess.

4. A rupture of a large blood-vessel in the lungs, attended with external or internal hæmorrhage. *Sudden* and *unexpected* death in a consumption is generally induced by this, or the preceding cause.

5. Madness. The cough and expectoration cease with this disease. It generally carries off the patient in a week or ten days.

6. A pleurisy, brought on by exposure to cold.

7. A typhus fever, attended with tremors, twitchings of the tendons, and a dry tongue.

8. Swelled hands, feet, legs, thighs, and face.

9. An apthous sore throat.

10. Great and tormenting pains, sometimes of a spasmodic nature in the limbs.

In a majority of the fatal cases of consumption, which I have seen, the passage out of life has been attended with pain; but I have seen many persons die with it, in whom all the above symptoms were so lenient, or so completely mitigated by opium, that death resembled a quiet transition from a waking, to a sleeping state.

I cannot conclude this inquiry without adding, that the author of it derived from his paternal ancestors a predisposition to the pulmonary consumption, and that between the 18th and 43d years of his age, he has occasionally been afflicted with many of the symptoms of that disease which he has described. By the constant and faithful use of many of the remedies which he has recommended, he now, in the 61st year of his age, enjoys nearly an uninterrupted exemption from pulmonary complaints. In humble gratitude, therefore, to that BEING, who condescends to be called the preserver of men, he thus publicly devotes this result of his experience and inquiries to the benefit of such of his fellow-creatures as may be afflicted with the same disease, sincerely wishing that they may be as useful to them, as they have been to the author.

Footnotes:

[17] Vol. I. p. 199.

[18] Sir George Baker relates, in the second volume of the Medical Transactions, that Dr. Blanchard had informed him, that he had seen the

consumption brought on ten persons out of ninety, by excessive purging used to prepare the body for the small-pox. I have seen a case of consumption in a youth of 17, from the spitting produced by the intemperate use of segars.

[19] Dr. Lind says, that out of 360 patients whom he attended between July 1st, 1758, and July 1st, 1760, in consumptions, the disease was brought on *one fourth* of them by falls, bruises, and strains, received a year or two before the disease made its appearance.

[20] Treatise of the Nature and Cure of Consumptions. Exercitation X.

[21] See Med. Com. Vol. II.

[22] Clinical and Anatomical Observations, p. 26, 27. See also Morgagni, letter xxii. 21.

[23] Pages 7, 8.

[24] The three last-mentioned symptoms are taken notice of by Dr. Bennet, in his Treatise upon the Nature and Cure of the Consumption, as *precursors* of the disease. Dr. Boerhaave used to tell his pupils that they had never deceived him.

[25] I have seen the *hoarseness* in one case the first symptom of approaching consumption. In this symptom it preserves the analogy of pneumony, which often comes on with a hoarseness, and sometimes with paraphonia.

[26] Observations on Scrophulous Affections.

[27] Prunus Virginiana.

[28] An Account of the Effects of Common Salt in the Cure of Hæmoptysis.

[29] Vol. I. p. 204.

[30] Medical Repository of New-York. Vol. V.

[31] Inquiry into the Diseases and Remedies of the Indians of North-America; and a comparative view of their diseases and remedies with those of civilized nations. Vol. I.

[32] Thoughts on the Pulmonary Consumption. Vol. I.

[33] The bad effects of *inconstant* exercise have been taken notice of in the gout. Dr. Sydenham says, when it is used only by fits and starts in this disease, it does harm.

[34] Medicina Gymnastica, p. 116.

OBSERVATIONS
ON
THE SYMPTOMS AND CURE
OF
DROPSIES.

Whether we admit the exhaling and absorbing vessels to be affected in general dropsies by preternatural debility, palsy, or rupture, or by a retrograde motion of their fluids, it is certain that their exhaling and absorbing power is materially affected by too much, or too little action in the arterial system. That too little action in the arteries should favour dropsical effusions, has been long observed; but it has been less obvious, that the same effusions are sometimes promoted, and their absorption prevented, by too much action in these vessels. That this fact should have escaped our notice is the more remarkable, considering how long we have been accustomed to seeing serous swellings in the joints in the acute rheumatism, and copious, but partial effusions of water in the form of sweat, in every species of inflammatory fever.

It is nothing new that the healthy action of one part, should depend upon the healthy action of another part of the system. We see it in many of the diseases of the nerves and brain. The tetanus is cured by exciting a tone in the arterial system; madness is cured by lessening the action of the arteries by copious blood-letting; and epilepsy and hysteria are often mitigated by the moderate use of the same remedy.

By too much action in the arterial system, I mean a certain morbid excitement in the arteries, accompanied by preternatural force, which is obvious to the sense of touch. It differs from the morbid excitement of the arteries, which takes place in common inflammatory fevers, in being attended by less febrile heat, and with little or no pain in the head or limbs. The thirst is nearly the same in this state of dropsy, as in inflammatory fevers. I include here those dropsies only in which the whole system is affected by what is called a hydropic diathesis.

That debility should, under certain circumstances, dispose to excessive action, and that excessive action should occur in one part of the body, at the same time that debility prevailed in every other, are abundantly evident from the history and phenomena of many diseases. Inflammatory fever, active hæmorrhages, tonic gout, asthma, apoplexy, and palsy, however much they are accompanied by excessive action in the arterial system, are always preceded by original debility, and are always accompanied by obvious debility in every other part of the system.

But it has been less observed by physicians that an undue force or excess of action occurs in the arterial system in certain dropsies, and that the same theory which explains the union of predisposing and nearly general debility, with a partial excitement and preternatural action in the arterial system, in the diseases before-mentioned, will explain the symptoms and cure of certain dropsies.

That debility predisposes to every state of dropsy, is evident from the history of all the remote and occasional causes which produce them. It will be unnecessary to mention these causes, as they are to be found in all our systems of physic. Nor will it be necessary to mention any proofs of the existence of debility in nearly every part of the body. It is too plain to be denied. I shall only mention the symptoms which indicate a morbid excitement and preternatural action of the arterial system. These are,

1. A *hard*, *full*, and *quick* pulse. This symptom, I believe, is more common in dropsies than is generally supposed, for many physicians visit and examine patients in these diseases, without feeling the pulse. Dr. Home mentions the *frequency* of the pulse, in the patients whose cures he has recorded[35], but he takes no notice of its force except in two cases. Dr. Zimmerman, in his account of the dropsy which terminated the life of Frederick II, of Prussia, tells us that he found his pulse *hard* and *full*. I have repeatedly found it full and hard in every form of dropsy, and more especially in the first stage of the disease. Indeed I have seldom found it otherwise in the beginning of the dropsy of the breast.

2. *Sizy blood*. This has been taken notice of by many practical writers, and has very justly been ascribed, under certain circumstances of blood-letting, to an excessive action of the vessels upon the blood.

3. *Alternation of dropsies with certain diseases which were evidently accompanied by excess of action in the arterial system.* I have seen anasarca alternate with vertigo, and both ascites and anasarca alternate with tonic madness. A case of nearly the same kind is related by Dr. Mead. Dr. Grimes, of Georgia, informed me that he had seen a tertian fever, in which the intermissions were attended with dropsical swellings all over the body, which suddenly disappeared in every accession of a paroxysm of the fever.

4. *The occasional connection of certain dropsies with diseases evidently of an inflammatory nature*, particularly pneumony, rheumatism, and gout.

5. Spontaneous *hæmorrhages* from the lungs, hæmorrhodial vessels, and nose, cases of which shall be mentioned hereafter, when we come to treat of the cure of dropsies.

6. *The appearance of dropsies in the winter and spring, in habits previously affected by the intermitting fever.* The debility produced by this state of fever, frequently disposes to inflammatory diathesis, as soon as the body is exposed to the alternate action of heat and cold, nor is this inflammatory diathesis always laid aside, by the transition of the intermitting fever into a dropsy, in the succeeding cold weather.

7. *The injurious effects of stimulating medicines in certain dropsies,* prove that there exists in them, at times, too much action in the blood-vessels. Dr. Tissot, in a letter to Dr. Haller, "De Variolis, apoplexia, et hydrope," condemns, in strong terms, the use of opium in the dropsy. Now the bad effects of this medicine in dropsies, must have arisen from its having been given in cases of too much action in the arterial system; for opium, we know, increases, by its stimulating qualities, the action and tone of the blood-vessels, and hence we find, it has been prescribed with success in dropsies of too little action in the system.

8. *The termination of certain fevers in dropsies in which blood-letting was not used.* This has been ascertained by many observations. Dr. Wilkes relates[36], that after "an epidemical fever, which began in Kidderminster, in 1728, and soon afterwards spread, not only over Great Britain, but all Europe, more people died dropsical in three years, than did perhaps in twenty or thirty years before," probably from the neglect of bleeding in the fever.

But the existence of too much action in the arterial system in certain dropsies, will appear more fully from the history of the effects of the remedies which have been employed either by design or accident in the cure of these diseases. I shall first mention the remedies which have been used with success in tonic or inflammatory dropsies; and afterwards mention those which have been given with success in dropsies of a weak action in the arteries. I have constantly proposed to treat only of the theory and cure of dropsies in general, without specifying any of the numerous names it derives from the different parts of the body in which they may be seated; but in speaking of the remedies which have been used with advantage in both the tonic and atonic states, I shall occasionally mention the name or seat of the dropsy in which the remedy has done service.

The first remedy that I shall mention for dropsies is *blood-letting.* Dr. Hoffman and Dr. Home both cured dropsies accompanied by pulmonic congestion by means of this remedy. Dr. Monroe quotes a case of dropsy from Sponius, in which bleeding succeeded, but not till after it had been used twenty times[37]. Mr. Cruikshank relates a case[38] of accidental bleeding, which confirms the efficacy of blood-letting in these diseases. He tells us that he attended a patient with dropsical swellings in his legs, who had had a hoarseness for two years. One morning, in stooping to buckle his shoes, he bursted a blood-vessel in his lungs, from which he lost a quart of blood; in consequence of which, both the swellings and the hoarseness went off gradually, and he continued well two years afterwards. I have known one case in which spontaneous hæmorrhages from the hæmorrhodial vessels, and from the nose, suddenly reduced universal dropsical swellings. In this patient there had been an uncommon tension and fulness in the pulse.

I could add the histories of many cures of anasarca and ascites, performed by means of blood-letting, not only by myself, but by a number of respectable physicians in the United States. Indeed I conceive this remedy to be as much indicated by a tense and full pulse in those forms of dropsy, as it is in a pleurisy, or in any other common inflammatory disease.

In those deplorable cases of hydrothorax, which do not admit of a radical cure, I have given temporary relief, and thereby protracted life, by taking away occasionally a few ounces of blood. Had Dr. Zimmerman used this remedy in the case of the king of Prussia, I cannot help thinking from the account which the doctor gives us of the diet and pulse of his royal patient, that he would have lessened his sufferings much more than by plentiful doses of dandelion; for I take it for granted, from the candour and integrity which the doctor discovered in all his visits to the king, that he did not expect that dandelion, or any other medicine, would cure him.

Although a *full* and *tense* pulse is always an indication of the necessity of bleeding; yet I can easily conceive there may be such congestions, and such a degree of stimulus to the arterial system, as to produce a depressed, or a *low* or *weak* pulse. Two cases of this kind are related by Dr. Monroe, one of which was cured by bleeding. The same symptom of a low and weak pulse is often met with in the *first* stage of pneumony, and apoplexy, and is only to be removed by the plentiful use of the same remedy.

II. *Vomits* have often been given with advantage in dropsies. Dr. Home says, that squills were useful in these diseases only when they produced a vomiting. By abstracting excitement and action from the arterial system, it disposes the lymphatics to absorb and discharge large quantities of water. The efficacy of vomits in promoting the absorption of stagnating fluids is not confined to dropsies. Mr. Hunter was once called to visit a patient in whom he found a bubo in such a state that he purposed to open it the next day. In the mean while, the patient went on board of a vessel, where he was severely affected by sea-sickness and vomiting; in consequence of which the bubo disappeared, and the patient recovered without the use of the knife.

Mr. Cruikshank further mentions a case[39] of a swelling in the knee being nearly cured by a patient vomiting eight and forty hours, in consequence of his taking a large dose of the salt of tartar instead of soluble tartar.

III. *Purges*. The efficacy of this remedy, in the cure of dropsies, has been acknowledged by physicians in all ages and countries. Jalap, calomel, scammony, and gamboge, are often preferred for this purpose; but I have heard of two cases of ascites being cured by a table spoonful of sweet oil taken every day. It probably acted only as a gentle laxative. The cream of tartar, so highly commended by Dr. Home, seems to act *chiefly* in the same way. Gherlius, from whom Dr. Home learned the use of this medicine, says, that all the persons whom he cured by it were in the vigour of life, and that their diseases had been only of a few months continuance. From these two circumstances, it is most probable they were dropsies of great morbid action in the arterial system. He adds further, that the persons who were cured by this medicine, were reduced very low by the use of it. Dr. Home says that it produced the same effect upon the patients whom he cured by it, in the infirmary of Edinburgh. Dr. Sydenham prefers gentle to drastic purges, and recommends the exhibition of them every day. Both drastic and gentle purges act by diminishing the action of the arterial system, and thereby promote the absorption and discharge of water. That purges promote absorption, we learn not only from their effects in dropsies, but from an experiment related by Mr. Cruikshank[40], of a man who acquired several ounces of weight after the operation of a purge. The absorption in this case was from the atmosphere. So great is the effect of purges in promoting absorption, that Mr. Hunter supposes the matter of a gonorrhœa, or of topical venereal ulcers to be conveyed by them in some instances into every part of the body.

IV. *Certain medicines*, which, by lessening the *action of the arterial system*, favour the absorption and evacuation of water. The only medicines of this class which I shall name are *nitre, cream of tartar*, and *foxglove*.

1. Two ounces of nitre dissolved in a pint of water, and a wine-glass full of it taken three times a-day have performed perfect cures, in two cases of ascites, which have come under my notice. I think I have cured two persons of anasarca, by giving one scruple of the same medicine three times a-day for several weeks. The two last cures were evidently dropsies of violent action in the arterial system. Where nitre has been given in atonic dropsies it has generally been useless, and sometimes done harm. I have seen one instance of an incurable diarrhœa after tapping, which I suspected arose from the destruction of the tone of the stomach and bowels, by large and long continued doses of nitre, which the patient had previously taken by the

advice of a person who had been cured by that remedy. To avoid this, or any other inconvenience from the use of nitre in dropsies, it should be given at first in small doses, and should always be laid aside, if it should prove ineffectual after having been given two or three weeks.

2. I can say nothing of the efficacy of *cream of tartar* in dropsies from my own experience, where it has not acted as a purge. Perhaps my want of decision upon this subject has arisen only from my not having persisted in the use of it for the same length of time which is mentioned by Dr. Home.

3. There are different opinions concerning the efficacy of foxglove in dropsies. From the cases related by Dr. Withering, it appears to have done good; but from those related by Dr. Lettsom[41] it seems to have done harm. I suspect the different accounts of those two gentlemen have arisen from their having given it in different states of the system, or perhaps from a difference in the quality of the plant from causes mentioned in another place[42]. I am sorry to add further, that after many trials of this medicine I have failed in most of the cases in which I have given it. I have discharged the water in three instances by it, but the disease returned, and my patients finally died. I can ascribe only one complete cure to its use, which was in the year 1789, in a young man in the Pennsylvania hospital, of five and thirty years of age, of a robust habit, and plethoric pulse.

Where medicines have once been in use, and afterwards fall into disrepute, as was the case with the foxglove, I suspect the cases in which they were useful, to have been either few or doubtful, and that the cases in which they had done harm, were so much more numerous and unequivocal, as justly to banish them from the materia medica.

V. *Hard labour*, or exercise in such a degree as to produce fatigue, have, in several instances, cured the dropsy. A dispensary patient, in this city, was cured of this disease by sawing wood. And a patient in an ascites under my care in the Pennsylvania hospital, had his belly reduced seven inches in circumference in one day, by the labour of carrying wood from the yard into the hospital. A second patient belonging to the Philadelphia dispensary was cured by walking to Lancaster, 66 miles from the city, in the middle of winter. The efficacy of travelling in this disease, in cold weather, is taken notice of by Dr. Monroe, who quotes a case from Dr. Holler, of a French merchant, who was cured of a dropsy by a journey from Paris to England, in the winter season. It would seem, that in these two cases, the *cold* co-operated as a sedative with the fatigue produced by labour or exercise, in reducing the tone of the arterial system.

VI. *Low diet*. I have heard of a woman who was cured of a dropsy by eating nothing but boiled beans for three weeks, and drinking nothing but the water in which they had been boiled. Many other cases of the good effects of low diet in dropsies are to be found in the records of medicine.

VII. *Thirst.* This cruel remedy acts by debilitating the system in two ways: 1st, by abstracting the stimulus of distention; and, 2dly, by preventing a supply of fresh water to replace that which is discharged by the ordinary emunctories of nature.

VIII. *Fasting.* An accidental circumstance, related by sir John Hawkins, in the life of Dr. Johnson, first led me to observe the good effects of fasting in the dropsy. If the fact alluded to stood alone under the present head of this essay, it would be sufficient to establish the existence of too much action, and the efficacy of debilitating remedies in certain dropsies. I am the more disposed to lay a good deal of stress upon this fact, as it was the clue which conducted me out of the labyrinth of empirical practice, in which I had been bewildered for many years, and finally led me to adopt the principles and practice which I am now endeavouring to establish. The passage which contains this interesting fact is as follows: "A few days after (says sir John) he [meaning Dr. Johnson] sent for me, and informed me, that he had discovered in himself the symptoms of a dropsy, and, indeed, his very much increased bulk, and the swollen appearance of his legs, seemed to indicate no less. It was on Thursday that I had this conversation with him; in the course thereof he declared, that he intended to devote the whole of the next day to *fasting*, humiliation, and such other devotional exercises as became a man in his situation. On the Saturday following I made him a visit, and, upon entering his room, I observed in his countenance such a serenity as indicated, that some remarkable crisis of his disease had produced a change in his feelings. He told me that, pursuant to the resolution he had mentioned to me, he had spent the preceding day in an abstraction from all worldly concerns; that to prevent interruption he had in the morning ordered *Frank* [his servant] not to admit any one to him, and, the better to enforce the charge, had added these awful words, *for your master is preparing himself to die.* He then mentioned to me, that in the course of this exercise he found himself relieved from the disease which had been growing upon him, and was becoming very oppressive, viz. the *dropsy*, by the gradual evacuation of water, to the amount of *twenty pints*, a like instance whereof he had never before experienced." Sir John Hawkins ascribes this immense discharge of water to the influence of Dr. Johnson's prayers; but he neglects to take notice, that these prayers were answered, in this instance, as they are in many others, in a perfect consistence with the common and established laws of nature.

To satisfy myself that this discharge of water, in the case of Dr. Johnson, was produced by the fasting only, I recommended it, soon after I read the above account, to a gentlewoman whom I was then attending in an ascites. I was delighted with the effects of it. Her urine, which for some time before had not exceeded half a pint a-day, amounted to *two quarts* on the day she fasted. I repeated the same prescription once a week for several weeks, and each time was informed of an increase of urine, though it was considerably less in the last experiments than in the first. Two patients in an ascites, to whom I prescribed the same remedy, in the Pennsylvania hospital, the one in the winter of 1790, and the other in the winter of 1792, exhibited proofs in the presence of many of the students of the university, equally satisfactory of the efficacy of fasting in suddenly increasing the quantity of urine.

IX. *Fear.* This passion is evidently of a debilitating nature, and, therefore, it has frequently afforded an accidental aid in the cure of dropsies, of too much action. I suspect, that the fear of death, which was so distinguishing a part of the character of Dr. Johnson, added a good deal to the efficacy of fasting, in procuring the immense discharge of water before-mentioned. In support of the efficacy of fear simply applied, in discharging water from the body in dropsies, I shall mention the following facts.

In a letter which I received from Dr. John Pennington, dated Edinburgh, August 3, 1790, I was favoured with the following communication. "Since the conversation I had with you on the subject of the dropsy, I feel more and more inclined to adopt your opinion. I can furnish you with a fact which I learned from a Danish sailor, on my passage to this country, which is much in favour of your doctrine. A sailor in an ascites, fell off the end of the yard into the sea; the weather being calm, he was taken up unhurt, but, to use the sailor's own words, who told me the story, he was *frightened half to death*, and as soon as he was taken out of the water, he discharged a gallon of urine or more. A doctor on board ascribed this large evacuation to sea bathing, and accordingly ordered the man to be dipped in the sea every morning, much against his will, for, my informant adds, that he had not forgotten his fall, and that in four weeks he was perfectly well. I think this fact can only be explained on your principles. The sedative operation of *fear* was, no doubt, the cause of his cure."

There is an account of an ascites being cured by a fall from an open chaise, recorded in the third volume of the Medical Memoirs, by M. Lowdell. I have heard of a complete recovery from dropsy, having suddenly followed a fall from a horse. In both these cases, the cures were probably the effects of fear.

Dr. Hall, of York-town, in Pennsylvania, informed me, that he had been called to visit a young woman of 19 years of age, who had taken all the usual remedies for ascites without effect. He at once proposed to her the operation of tapping. To this she objected, but so great was the *fear* of this operation, which the proposal of it suddenly excited in her mind, that it brought on a plentiful discharge of urine, which in a few days perfectly removed her disease.

On the 27th of August, 1790, I visited a gentlewoman in this city with the late Dr. Jones, in an ascites. We told her for the first time, that she could not be relieved without being tapped. She appeared to be much terrified upon hearing our opinion, and said that she would consider of it. I saw her two days afterwards, when she told me, with a smile on her countenance, that she hoped she should get well without tapping, for that she had discharged two quarts of water in the course of the day after we had advised her to submit to that operation. For many days before, she had not discharged more than two or three gills in twenty-four hours. The operation, notwithstanding, was still indicated, and she submitted to be tapped a few days afterwards.

I tapped the same gentlewoman a second time, in January, 1791. She was much terrified while I was preparing for the operation, and fainted immediately after the puncture was made. The second time that I visited her after the operation was performed, she told me (without being interrogated on that subject), that she had discharged a pint and a half of urine, within twenty minutes after I left the room on the day I tapped her. What made this discharge the more remarkable was, she had not made more than a table spoonful of water in a day, for several days before she was tapped.

I have seen similar discharges of urine in two other cases of tapping which have come under my notice, but they resembled so nearly those which have been mentioned, that it will be unnecessary to record them.

But the influence of fear upon the system, in the dropsy, extends far beyond the effects which I have ascribed to it. Dr. Currie, of this city, informed me that he called, some years ago, by appointment, to tap a woman. He no sooner entered the room than he observed her, as he thought, to faint away. He attempted to recover her, but to no purpose. She died of a sudden paroxysm of fear.

It is a matter of surprise, that we should have remained so long ignorant of the influence of fear upon the urinary organs in dropsies, after having been so long familiar with the same effect of that passion in the hysteria.

X. *A recumbent posture of the body.* It is most useful when the dropsy is seated in the lower limbs. I have often seen, with great pleasure, the happiest effects from this prescription in a few days.

XI. *Punctures.* These, when made in the legs and feet, often discharge in eight and forty hours the water of the whole body. I have never seen a mortification produced by them. As they are not followed by inflammation, they should be preferred to blisters, which are sometimes used for the same purpose.

I cannot dismiss the remedies which discharge water from the body through the urinary passages, without taking notice, that they furnish an additional argument in favour of blood-letting in dropsies, for they act, not by discharging the stagnating water, but by creating such a plentiful secretion in the kidneys from the serum of the circulating blood, as to make room for the absorption and conveyance of the stagnating water into the blood-vessels.

Now the same effect may be produced in all tonic or inflammatory dropsies, with more certainty and safety, by means of blood-letting.

In recommending the antiphlogistic treatment of certain dropsies, I must here confine myself to the dropsies of such climates as dispose to diseases of great morbid action in the system. I am satisfied that it will often be proper in the middle and eastern states of America; and I have lately met with two observations, which show that it has been used with success at Vienna, in Germany. Dr. Stoll tells us, that, in the month of January, 1780, "Hydropic and asthmatic patients discovered more or less marks of inflammatory diathesis, and that blood was drawn from them with a sparing hand with advantage;" and in the month of November, of the same year, he says, "The stronger diuretics injured dropsical patients in this season; but an antiphlogistic drink, composed of a quart of the decoction of grass, with two ounces of simple oxymel, and nitre and cream of tartar, of each a drachm, did service[43]." It is probable that the same difference should be observed between the treatment of dropsies in warm and cold climates that is observed in the treatment of fevers. The tonic action probably exists in the system in both countries. In the former it resembles the tides which are suddenly produced by a shower of rain, and as suddenly disappear; whereas, in the latter, it may be compared to those tides which are produced by the flow and gradual addition of water from numerous streams, and which continue for days and weeks together to exhibit marks of violence in every part of their course.

I come now to say a few words upon atonic dropsies, or such as are accompanied with a feeble morbid action in the blood-vessels. This morbid action is essential to the nature of dropsies, for we never see them take place without it. This is obvious from the absence of swellings after famine, marasmus, and in extreme old age, in each of which there exists the lowest degree of debility, but no morbid action in the blood-vessels. These atonic or typhus dropsies may easily be distinguished from those which have been described, by occurring in habits naturally weak; by being produced by the operation of chronic causes; by a weak and quick pulse; and by little or no preternatural heat or thirst.

The remedies for atonic dropsies are all such stimulating substances as increase the action of the arterial system, or determine the fluids to the urinary organs. These are,

I. *Bitter* and *aromatic substances* of all kinds, exhibited in substance or in infusions of wine, spirit, beer, or water.

II. *Certain acrid vegetables,* such as scurvy-grass, horse-radish, mustard, water-cresses, and garlic. I knew an old man who was perfectly cured of an anasarca, by eating water-cresses, on bread and butter.

III. *Opium.* The efficacy of this medicine in dropsies has been attested by Dr. Willis, and several other practical writers. It seems to possess almost an exclusive power of acting alike upon the arterial, the lymphatic, the glandular, and the nervous systems.

IV. *Metallic tonics,* such as chalybeate medicines of all kinds, and the mild preparations of copper and mercury. I once cured an incipient ascites and anasarca by large doses of the rust of iron; and I have cured many dropsies by giving mercury in such quantities as to excite a plentiful salivation. I have, it is true, often given it without effect, probably from my former ignorance of the violent action of the arteries, which so frequently occurs in dropsies, and in which cases mercury must necessarily have done harm.

V. *Diuretics,* consisting of alkaline salts, nitre, and the oxymels of squills and colchicum. It is difficult to determine how far these medicines produce their salutary effects by acting directly upon the kidneys. It is remarkable that these organs are seldom affected in dropsies, and that their diseases are rarely followed by dropsical effusions in any part of the body.

VI. *Generous diet,* consisting of animal food, rendered cordial by spices; also sound old wine.

VII. *Diluting drinks* taken in such large quantities as to excite the action of the vessels by the stimulus of distention. This effect has been produced, sir George Baker informs us, by means of large draughts of simple water, and of cyder and water[44]. The influence of distention in promoting absorption is evident in the urinary and gall bladders, which frequently return their contents to the blood by the lymphatics, when they are unable to discharge them through their usual emunctories. Is it not probable that the distention produced by the large quantities of liquids which we are directed to administer after giving the foxglove, may have been the means of performing some of those cures of dropsies, which have been ascribed to that remedy?

VIII. *Pressure.* Bandages bound tightly around the belly and limbs, sometimes prevent the increase or return of dropsical swellings. The influence of pressure upon the action of the lymphatics appears in the absorption of bone which frequently follows the pressure of contiguous tumours, also in the absorption of flesh which follows the long pressure of certain parts of the body upon a sick bed.

IX. *Frictions*, either by means of a dry, or oiled hand, or with linen or flannel impregnated with volatile and other stimulating substances. I have found evident advantages from following the advice of Dr. Cullen, by rubbing the lower extremities *upwards*, and that only in the *morning*. I have been at a loss to account for the manner in which sweet oil acts, when applied to dropsical swellings. If it act by what is improperly called a sedative power upon the blood-vessels, it will be more proper in tonic than atonic dropsies; but if it act by closing the pores, and thereby preventing the absorption of moisture from the air, it will be very proper in the state of dropsy which is now under consideration. It is in this manner that Dr. Cullen supposes that sweet oil, when applied to the body, cures that state of diabetes in which nothing but insipid water is discharged from the bladder.

X. *Heat*, applied either separately or combined with moisture in the form of warm or vapour baths, has been often used with success in dropsies of too little action. Dampier, in his voyage round the world, was cured of a dropsy by means of a copious sweat, excited by burying himself in a bed of warm sand. Warm fomentations to the legs, rendered moderately stimulating by the addition of saline or aromatic substances, have often done service in the atonic dropsical swellings of the lower extremities.

XI. The *cold bath*. I can say nothing in favour of the efficacy of this remedy in dropsies, from my own experience. Its good effects seem to depend wholly on its increasing the excitability of the system to common stimuli, by the diminution of its excitement. If this be the case, I would ask, whether *fear* might not be employed for the same purpose, and thus become as useful in atonic, as it was formerly proved to be in tonic dropsies?

XII. *Wounds*, whether excited by cutting instruments or by fire, provided they excite inflammation and action in the arteries, frequently cure atonic dropsies. The good effects of inflammation and action in these cases, appear in the cure of hydrocele by means of the needle, or the caustic.

XIII. *Exercise*. This is probably as necessary in the atonic dropsy, as it is in the consumption, and should never be omitted when a patient is able to take it. The passive exercises of swinging, and riding in a carriage, are most proper in the lowest stage of the disease; but as soon as the patient's strength will admit of it, he should ride on horseback. A journey should be preferred, in this disease, to short excursions from home.

XIV. A *recumbent posture of the body* should always be advised during the intervals of exercise, when the swellings are seated in the lower extremities.

XV. *Punctures in the legs and feet* afford the same relief in general dropsy, accompanied with a weak action in the blood-vessels, that has been ascribed to them in dropsies of an opposite character.

In the application of each of the remedies which have been mentioned, for the cure of both tonic and atonic dropsies, great care should be taken to use them in such a manner, as to accommodate them to the strength and excitability of the patient's system. The most powerful remedies have often been rendered *hurtful*, by being given in too large doses in the beginning, and *useless*, by being given in too small doses in the subsequent stages of the disease.

I have avoided saying any thing of the usual operations for discharging water from different parts of the body, as my design was to treat only of the symptoms and cure of those dropsies which affect the whole system. I shall only remark, that if tapping and punctures have been more successful in the early, than in the late stage of these diseases, it is probably because the sudden or gradual evacuation of water takes down that excessive action in the arterial system, which is most common in their early stage, and thereby favours the speedy restoration of healthy action in the exhaling or lymphatic vessels.

Thus have I endeavoured to prove, that two different states of action take place in dropsies, and have mentioned the remedies which are proper for each of them under separate heads. But I suspect that dropsies are often connected with a certain *intermediate* or mixed action in the arterial system, analogous to the typhoid action which takes place in certain fevers. I am led to adopt this opinion, not only from having observed mixed action to be so universal in most of the diseases of the arterial and nervous system, but because I have so frequently observed dropsical swellings to follow the scarlatina, and the puerperile fever, two diseases which appear to derive their peculiar character from a mixture of excessive and moderate *force*, combined with irregularity of action in the arterial system. In dropsies of mixed action, where too much force prevails in the action of some, and too little in the action of other of the arterial fibres, the remedies must be debilitating or stimulating, according to the greater or less predominance of tonic or atonic diathesis in the arterial system.

I shall conclude this history of dropsies, and of the different and opposite remedies which have cured them, by the following observations.

1. We learn, in the first place, from what has been said, the impropriety and even danger of prescribing stimulating medicines indiscriminately in every case of dropsy.

2. We are taught, by the facts which have been mentioned, the reason why physicians have differed so much in their accounts of the same remedies, and

why the same remedies have operated so differently in the hands of the same physicians. It is because they have been given without a reference to the different states of the system, which have been described. Dr. Sydenham says, that he cured the first dropsical patient he was called to, by frequent purges. He began to exult in the discovery, as he thought, of a certain cure for dropsies, but his triumph was of short duration. The same remedy failed in the next case in which he prescribed it. The reason probably was, the dropsy in the first case was of a tonic, but in the second of an atonic nature; for the latter was an ascites from a quartan ague. It is agreeable, however, to discover, from the theory of dropsies which has been laid down, that all the different remedies for these diseases have been proper in their nature, and improper only in the state of the system in which they have been given. As the discovery of truth in religion reconciles the principles of the most opposite sects, so the discovery of truth in medicine reconciles the most opposite modes of practice. It would be happy if the inquirers after truth in medicine should be taught, by such discoveries, to treat each other with tenderness and respect, and to wait with patience till accident, or time, shall combine into one perfect and consistent system, all the contradictory facts and opinions, about which physicians have been so long divided.

3. If a state of great morbid action in the arteries has been demonstrated in dropsies, both from its symptoms and remedies, and if these dropsies are evidently produced by previous debility, who will deny the existence of a similar action in certain hæmorrhages, in gout, palsy, apoplexy, and madness, notwithstanding they are all the offspring of predisposing debility? And who will deny the efficacy of bleeding, purges, and other debilitating medicines in certain states of those diseases, that has seen the same medicines administered with success in certain dropsies? To reject bleeding, purging, and the other remedies for violent action in the system, in any of the above diseases, because that action was preceded by general debility, will lead us to reject them in the most acute inflammatory fevers, for these are as much the offspring of previous debility as dropsies or palsy. The previous debility of the former differs from that of the latter diseases, only in being of a more acute, or, in other words, of a shorter duration.

4. From the symptoms of tonic dropsy which have been mentioned, it follows, that the distinction of apoplexy into serous and sanguineous, affords no rational indication for a difference in the mode of treating that disease. If an effusion of serum in the thorax, bowels, or limbs, produce a hard and full pulse, it is reasonable to suppose that the same symptom will be produced by the effusion of serum in the brain. But the dissections collected by Lieutaud[45] place this opinion beyond all controversy. They prove that the symptoms of great and feeble morbid action, as they appear in the pulse, follow alike the effusion of serum and blood in the brain. This fact will admit

of an important application to the disease, which is to be the subject of the next inquiry.

5. From the influence which has been described, of the different states of action of the arterial system, upon the lymphatic vessels, in dropsies, we are led to reject the indiscriminate use of bark, mercury, and salt water, in the scrophula. When the action of the arteries is weak, those remedies are proper; but when an opposite state of the arterial system occurs, and, above all, when scrophulous tumours are attended with inflammatory ulcers, stimulating medicines of all kinds are hurtful. By alternating the above remedies with a milk and vegetable diet, according to the tonic, or atonic states of the arterial system, I have succeeded in the cure of a case of scrophula, attended by large ulcers in the inguinal glands, which had for several years resisted the constant use of the three stimulating remedies which have been mentioned.

6. Notwithstanding I have supposed dropsies to be connected with a peculiar state of force in the blood-vessels, yet I have not ventured to assert, that dropsies may not exist from an exclusive affection of the exhaling and absorbing vessels. I conceive this to be as possible, as for a fever to exist from an exclusive affection of the arteries, or a hysteria from an exclusive affection of the nervous system. Nothing, however, can be said upon this subject, until physiology and pathology have taught us more of the structure and diseases of the lymphatic vessels. Nor have I ventured further to assert, that there are not medicines which may act specifically upon the lymphatics, independently of the arteries. This I conceive to be as possible as for asafœtida to act chiefly upon the nerves, or ipecacuanha and jalap upon the alimentary canal, without affecting other parts of the system. Until such medicines are discovered, it becomes us to avail ourselves of the access to the lymphatics, which is furnished us through the medium of the arteries, by means of most of the remedies which have been mentioned.

7. If it should appear hereafter, that we have lessened the mortality of certain dropsies by the theory and practice which have been proposed, yet many cases of dropsy must still occur in which they will afford us no aid. The cases I allude to are dropsies from enclosing cysts, from the ossification of certain arteries, from schirri of certain viscera from large ruptures of exhaling or lymphatic vessels, from a peculiar and corrosive acrimony of the fluids, and, lastly, from an exhausted state of the whole system. The records of medicine furnish us with instances of death from each of the above causes. But let us not despair. It becomes a physician to believe, that there is no disease necessarily incurable; and that there exist in the womb of time, certain remedies for all those morbid affections, which elude the present limits of the healing art.

Footnotes:

[35] Medical Facts.

[36] Historical Essay on the Dropsy, p. 326.

[37] Treatise on the Dropsy.

[38] Treatise on the Lymphatics.

[39] Letter to Mr. Clare, p. 166.

[40] Letter to Mr. Clare, p. 117.

[41] Medical Memoirs, vol. II.

[42] Inquiry into the Causes and Cure of Pulmonary Consumption.

[43] Ratio Medendi Nosocomio Practico Vindobonensi, vol. iv. p. 56 and 99.

[44] The remark upon this fact by sir George, is worthy of notice, and implies much more than was probably intended by it. "When common means have failed, success has sometimes followed a method *directly contrary* to the established practice." Medical Transactions, vol. II.

[45] Historia Anatomica Medica, vol. II.

AN INQUIRY
INTO THE
CAUSES AND CURE
OF THE
INTERNAL DROPSY OF THE BRAIN.

Having, for many years, been unsuccessful in all the cases, except two, of internal dropsy of the brain, which came under my care, I began to entertain doubts of the common theory of this disease, and to suspect that the effusion of water should be considered only as the effect of a primary disease in the brain.

I mentioned this opinion to my colleague, Dr. Wistar, in the month of June, 1788, and delivered it the winter following in my lectures. The year afterwards I was confirmed in it, by hearing that the same idea had occurred to Dr. Quin. I have since read Dr. Quin's treatise on the dropsy of the brain with great pleasure, and consider it as the first dawn of light which has been shed upon it. In pursuing this subject, therefore, I shall avail myself of Dr. Quin's discoveries, and endeavour to arrange the facts and observations I have collected in such a manner, as to form a connected theory from them, which I hope will lead to a new and more successful mode of treating this disease.

I shall begin this inquiry by delivering a few general propositions.

1. The internal dropsy of the brain is a disease confined chiefly to children.

2. In children the brain is larger in proportion to other parts of the body, than it is in adults; and of course a greater proportion of blood is sent to it in childhood, than in the subsequent periods of life. The effects of this determination of blood to the brain appear in the mucous discharge from the nose, and in the sores on the head and behind the ears, which are so common in childhood.

3. In all febrile diseases, there is a preternatural determination of blood to the brain. This occurs in a more especial manner in children: hence the reason why they are so apt to be affected by convulsions in the eruptive fever of the small-pox, in dentition, in the diseases from worms, and in the first paroxysm of intermitting fevers.

4. In fevers of every kind, and in every stage of life, there is a disposition to effusion in that part to which there is the greatest determination. Thus, in inflammatory fever, effusions take place in the lungs and in the joints. In the bilious fever they occur in the liver, and in the gout in every part of the body. The matter effused is always influenced by the structure of the part in which it takes place.

These propositions being premised, I should have proceeded to mention the remote causes of this disease; but as this inquiry may possibly fall into the hands of some gentlemen who may not have access to the description of it as given by Dr. Whytt, Dr. Fothergill, and Dr. Quin, I shall introduce a history of its symptoms taken from the last of those authors. I prefer it to the histories by Dr. Whytt and Dr. Fothergill, as it accords most with the ordinary phenomena of this disease in the United States.

"In general, the patient is at first languid and inactive, often drowsy and peevish, but at intervals cheerful and apparently free from complaint. The appetite is weak, a nausea, and, in many cases, a vomiting, occurs once or twice in the day, and the skin is observed to be hot and dry towards the evenings: soon after these symptoms have appeared, the patient is affected with a sharp head-ach, chiefly in the fore-part, or, if not there, generally in the crown of the head: it is sometimes, however, confined to one side of the head, and, in that case, when the posture of the body is erect, the head often inclines to the side affected. We frequently find, also, that the head-ach alternates with the affection of the stomach; the vomiting being less troublesome when the pain is most violent, and *vice versâ*; other parts of the body are likewise subject to temporary attacks of pain, viz. the extremities, or the bowels, but more constantly the back of the neck, and between the scapulæ; in all such cases the head is more free from uneasiness.

"The patient dislikes the light at this period; cries much, sleeps little, and when he does sleep, he grinds his teeth, picks his nose, appears to be uneasy, and starts often, screaming as if he were terrified; the bowels are in the majority of cases very much confined, though it sometimes happens that they are in an opposite state: the pulse in this early stage of the disorder, does not usually indicate any material derangement.

"When the symptoms above-mentioned have continued for a few days, subject as they always are in this disease to great fluctuation, the axis of one eye is generally found to be turned in towards the nose; the pupil on this side is rather more dilated than the other; and when both eyes have the axes directed inwards (which sometimes happens), both pupils are larger than they are observed to be in the eyes of healthy persons: the vomiting becomes more constant, and the head-ach more excruciating; every symptom of fever

- 82 -

then makes its appearance, the pulse is frequent, and the breathing quick; exacerbations of the fever take place towards the evening, and the face is occasionally flushed; usually one cheek is much more affected than the other; temporary perspirations likewise break forth, which are not followed by any alleviation of distress; a discharge of blood from the nose, which sometimes appears about this period, is equally inefficacious.

"Delirium, and that of the most violent kind, particularly if the patient has arrived at the age of puberty, now takes place, and with all the preceding symptoms of fever, continues for a while to increase, until about fourteen days, often a much shorter space of time, shall have elapsed since the appearance of the symptoms, which were first mentioned in the above detail.

"The disease then undergoes that remarkable change, which sometimes suddenly points out the commencement of what has been called its second stage: the pulse becomes slow but unequal, both as to its strength, and the intervals between the pulsations; the pain of the head, or of whatever part had previously been affected, seems to abate, or at least the patient becomes apparently less sensible of it; the interrupted slumbers, or perpetual restlessness which prevailed during the earlier periods of the disorder, are now succeeded by an almost lethargetic torpor, the strabismus, and dilatation of the pupil increase, the patient lies with one, or both eyes half closed, which, when minutely examined, are often found to be completely insensible to light; the vomiting ceases; whatever food or medicine is offered is usually swallowed with apparent voracity; the bowels at this period generally remain obstinately costive.

"If every effort made by art fails to excite the sinking powers of life, the symptoms of what has been called the second stage are soon succeeded by others, which more certainly announce the approach of death. The pulse again becomes equal, but so weak and quick, that it is almost impossible to count it; a difficulty of breathing, nearly resembling the *stertor apoplecticus*, is often observed; sometimes the eyes are suffused with blood, the flushing of the face is more frequent than before, but of shorter duration, and followed by a deadly paleness; red spots, or blotches, sometimes appear on the body and limbs; deglutition becomes difficult, and convulsions generally close the scene. In one case, I may observe, the jaws of a child of four years of age were so firmly locked for more than a day before death, that it was impossible to introduce either food or medicine into his mouth; and, in another case, a hemiplegia, attended with some remarkable circumstances, occurred during the two days preceding dissolution.

"Having thus given as exact a history of *apoplexia hydrocephalica* as I could compile from the writings of others, and from my own observations, I should think myself guilty of imposition on my readers, if I did not caution them that it must be considered merely as a general outline: the human brain seems to be so extremely capricious (if the expression may be allowed) in the signals it gives to other parts of the system, of the injury it suffers throughout the course of this disease, that although every symptom above-mentioned does occasionally occur, and indeed few cases of the disease are to be met with, which do not exhibit many of them; yet it does not appear to me, that any one of them is constantly and inseparably connected with it."

To this history I shall add a few facts, which are the result of observations made by myself, or communicated to me by my medical brethren. These facts will serve to show that there are many deviations from the history of the disease which has been given, and that it is indeed, as Dr. Quin has happily expressed it, of **LQU]a truly proteiform" nature.

I have not found the dilated and insensible pupil, the puking, the delirium, or the strabismus, to attend universally in this disease.

I saw one case in which the appetite was unimpaired from the first to the last stage of the disease.

I have met with one case in which the disease was attended by blindness, and another by double vision.

I have observed an uncommon acuteness in hearing to attend two cases of this disease. In one of them the noise of the sparks which were discharged from a hiccory[** sic] fire, produced great pain and startings which threatened convulsions.

I have seen three cases in which the disease terminated in hemiplegia. In two of them it proved fatal in a few days; in the third it continued for nearly eighteen months.

I have met with one case in which no preternatural slowness or intermission was ever perceived in the pulse.

I have seen the disease in children of nearly all ages. I once saw it in a child of six weeks old. It was preceded by the cholera infantum. The sudden deaths which we sometimes observe in infancy, I believe, are often produced by this disease. Dr. Stoll is of the same opinion. He calls it, when it appears in this form, "apoplexia infantalis[46]."

In the month of March, 1771, I obtained a gill of water from the ventricles of the brain of a negro girl of nine years of age, who died of this disease, who complained in no stage of it of a pain in her head or limbs, nor of a sick stomach. The disease in this case was introduced suddenly by a pain in the breast, a fever, and the usual symptoms of a catarrh.

Dr. Wistar informed me, that he had likewise met with a case of internal dropsy of the brain, in which there was a total absence of pain in the head.

Dr. Carson informed me, that he had attended a child in this disease that discovered, for some days before it died, the symptom of hydrophobia.

Dr. Currie obtained, by dissection, seven ounces of water from the brain of a child which died of this disease; in whom, he assured me, no dilatation of the pupil, strabismus, sickness, or loss of appetite had attended, and but very little head-ach.

The causes which induce this disease, act either *directly* on the brain, or *indirectly* upon it, through the medium of the whole system.

The causes which act *directly* on the brain are falls or bruises upon the head, certain positions of the body, and childish plays which bring on congestion or inflammation, and afterwards an effusion of water in the brain. I have known it brought on in a child by falling into a cellar upon its feet.

The *indirect* causes of this disease are more numerous, and more frequent, though less suspected, than those which have been mentioned. The following diseases of the whole system appear to act indirectly in producing an internal dropsy of the brain.

1. *Intermitting, remitting,* and *continual* fevers. Of the effects of these fevers in inducing this disease, many cases are recorded by Lieutaud[47].

My former pupil, Dr. Woodhouse, has furnished me with a dissection, in which the disease was evidently the effect of the remitting fever. That state of continual fever which has been distinguished by the name of typhus, is often the remote cause of this disease. The languor and weakness in all the muscles of voluntary motion, the head-ach, the inclination to rest and sleep, and the disposition to be disturbed, or terrified by dreams, which are said to be the precursors of water in the brain, I believe are frequently symptoms of a typhus fever which terminates in an inflammation, or effusion of water in the brain. The history which is given of the typhus state of fever in children by Dr. Butter[48], seems to favour this opinion.

2. The *rheumatism.* Of this I have known two instances. Dr. Lettsom has recorded a case from the same cause[49]. The pains in the limbs, which are supposed to be the effect, I suspect are frequently the cause of the disease.

3. The *pulmonary consumption.* Of the connection of this disease with an internal dropsy of the brain, Dr. Percival has furnished us with the following communication[50]: "Mr. C——'s daughter, aged nine years, after labouring under the phthisis pulmonalis four months, was affected with unusual pains

in her head. These rapidly increased, so as to occasion frequent screamings. The cough, which had before been extremely violent, and was attended with stitches in the breast, now abated, and in a few days ceased almost entirely. The pupils of the eyes became dilated, a strabismus ensued, and in about a week death put an end to her agonies. Whether this affection of the head arose from the effusion of water or of blood, is uncertain, but its influence on the state of the lungs is worthy of notice." Dr. Quin likewise mentions a case from Dr. Cullen's private practice, in which an internal dropsy of the brain followed a pulmonary consumption. Lieutaud mentions three cases of the same kind[51], and two, in which it succeeded a catarrh[52].

4. *Eruptive fevers.* Dr. Odier informs us[53], that he had seen four cases in which it had followed the small-pox, measles, and scarlatina. Dr. Lettsom mentions a case in which it followed the small-pox[54], and I have seen one in which it was obviously the effects of debility induced upon the system by the measles.

5. *Worms.* Notwithstanding the discharge of worms gives no relief in this disease, yet there is good reason to believe, that it has, in some instances, been produced by them. The morbid action continues in the brain, as in other cases of disease, after the cause which induced it, has ceased to act upon the body.

6. From the dissections of Lieutaud, Quin, and others, it appears further, that the internal dropsy of the brain has been observed to succeed each of the following diseases, viz. the colic, palsy, melancholy, dysentery, dentition, insolation, and scrophula, also the sudden healing of old sores. I have seen two cases of it from the last cause, and one in which it was produced by the action of the vernal sun alone upon the system.

From the facts which have been enumerated, and from dissections to be mentioned hereafter, it appears, that the disease in its first stage is the effect of causes which produce a less degree of that morbid action in the brain which constitutes phrenitis, and that its second stage is the effect of a less degree of that effusion, which produces serous apoplexy in adults. The former partakes of the nature of the chronic inflammation of Dr. Cullen, and of the asthenic inflammation of Dr. Brown. I have taken the liberty to call it *phrenicula*, from its being a diminutive species or state of phrenitis. It bears the same relation to phrenitis, when it arises from indirect causes, which pneumonicula does to pneumony; and it is produced nearly in the same manner as the pulmonary consumption, by debilitating causes which act primarily on the whole system. The peculiar size and texture of the brain seem to invite the inflammation and effusions which follow debility, to that organ in childhood, just as the peculiar structure and situation of the lungs invite the same morbid phænomena to them, after the body has acquired its growth, in youth and middle life. In the latter stage which has been mentioned, the internal dropsy of the brain partakes of some of the properties of apoplexy. It differs from it in being the effect of a *slow*, instead of a *sudden* effusion of water or blood, and in being the effect of causes which are of an acute instead of a chronic nature. In persons advanced beyond middle life, who are affected by this disease, it approaches to the nature of the common apoplexy, by a speedy termination in life or death. Dr. Cullen has called it simply by the name of "apoplexia hydrocephalica." I have preferred for its last stage the term of *chronic apoplexy*, for I believe with Dr. Quin, that it has no connection with a hydropic diathesis of the whole system. I am forced to adopt this opinion, from my having rarely seen it accompanied by dropsical effusions in other parts of the body, nor a general dropsy accompanied by an internal dropsy of the brain. No more occurs in this disease than takes place when hydrothorax follows an inflammation of the lungs, or when serous effusions follow an inflammation of the joints. I do not suppose that both inflammation and effusion always attend in this disease; on the contrary, dissections have shown some cases of inflammation, with little or no effusion, and some of effusion without inflammation. Perhaps this variety may have been produced by the different stages of the disease in which death and the inspection of the brain took place. Neither do I suppose, that the two stages which have been mentioned, always succeed each other in the common order of inflammation and effusion. In every case where the full tense, slow and intermitting pulse occurs, I believe there is inflammation; and as this state of the pulse occurs in most cases in the beginning of the disease, I suppose the inflammation, in most cases, to precede the effusion of water. I have met with only one case in which the slow and tense pulse was absent; and out of six dissections of patients whom I have lost by this disease, the brains of four of them exhibited marks of inflammation.

Mr. Davis discovered signs of inflammation, after death from this disease, to be universal. In eighteen or twenty dissections, he tells us, he found the pia mater always distended with blood[55]. Where signs of inflammation have not occurred, the blood-vessels had probably relieved themselves by the effusion of serum, or the morbid action of the blood-vessels had exceeded that grade of excitement, in which only inflammation can take place. I have seen one case of death from this disease, in which there was not more than a tea-spoonful of water in the ventricles of the brain. Dr. Quin mentions a similar case. Here death was induced by simple excess of excitement. The water which is found in the ventricles of the brain refuses to coagulate by heat, and is always pale in those diseases, in which the serum of the blood, in every other part of the body, is of a yellow colour.

In addition to these facts, in support of the internal dropsy of the brain being the effect of inflammation, I shall mention one more, communicated to me in a letter, dated July 17th, 1795, by my former pupil, Dr. Coxe, while he was prosecuting his studies in London. "It so happened (says my ingenious correspondent), that at the time of my receiving your letter, Dr. Clark was at the hospital. I read to him that part which relates to your success in the treatment of hydrocephalus internus. He was much pleased with it, and mentioned to me a fact which strongly corroborates your idea of its being a primary inflammation of the brain. This fact was, that upon opening, not long since, the head of a child that had died of this disease, he found between three and four ounces of water in the ventricles of the brain; also an inflammatory crust on the optic nerves, as thick as he had ever observed it on the intestines in a state of inflammation. The child lost its sight before it died. The crust accounted in a satisfactory manner for its blindness. Perhaps something similar may always be noticed in the dissections of such as die of this disease, in whom the eyes are much affected."

Having adopted the theory of this disease, which I have delivered, I resolved upon such a change in my practice as should accord with it. The first remedy indicated by it was

I. *Blood-letting.* I shall briefly mention the effects of this remedy in a few of the first cases in which I prescribed it.

CASE I.

On the 15th of November, 1790, I was called to visit the daughter of William Webb, aged four years, who was indisposed with a cough, a pain in her bowels, a coma, great sensibility of her eyes to light, costiveness, and a suppression of urine, a slow and irregular, but tense pulse, dilated pupils, but no head-ach. I found, upon inquiry, that she had received a hurt on her head by a fall, about seven weeks before I saw her. From this information, as well as from her symptoms, I had no doubt of the disease being the internal dropsy of the brain. I advised the loss of five ounces of blood, which gave her some relief. The blood was sizy. The next day she took a dose of jalap and calomel, which operated twelve times. On the 18th she lost four ounces more of blood, which was more sizy than that drawn on the 15th. From this time she mended rapidly. Her coma left her on the 20th, and her appetite returned; on the 21st she made a large quantity of turbid dark coloured urine. On the 22d her pulse became again a little tense, for which she took a gentle puke. On the 23d she had a natural stool. On the 24th her pupils appeared to be contracted to their natural size, and on the 30th I had the pleasure of seeing her seated at a tea-table in good health. Her pulse notwithstanding, was a little more active and tense than natural.

CASE II.

On the 24th of the same month, I was called to visit the son of John Cypher, in South-street, aged four years, who had been hurt about a month before, by a wound on his forehead with a brick-bat, the mark of which still appeared. He had been ill for near two weeks with coma, head-ach, colic, vomiting, and frequent startings in his sleep. His evacuations by stool and urine were suppressed; he had discharged three worms, and had had two convulsion fits just before I saw him. The pupil of the right eye was larger than that of the left. His pulse was full, tense, and slow, and intermitted every *fourth* stroke. The symptoms plainly indicated an internal dropsy of the brain. I ordered him to lose four or five ounces of blood. But three ounces of blood were drawn, which produced a small change in his pulse. It rendered the intermission of a pulsation perceptible only after every tenth stroke. On the 25th he lost five ounces of blood, and took a purge of calomel and jalap. On the 26th he was better. On the 27th the vomiting was troublesome, and his pulse was still full and tense, but regular. I ordered him to lose four ounces of blood. On the 28th his puking and head-ach continued; his pulse was a little tense, but regular; and his right pupil less dilated. On the 29th his head-ach and puking ceased, and he played about the room. On the 4th of December he grew worse; his head-ach and puking returned, with a hard pulse, for which I ordered him to lose five ounces of blood. On the 5th he was better, but on the 6th his head-ach and puking returned. On the 7th I ordered his forehead to be bathed frequently with vinegar, in which ice had been dissolved. On the 8th he was much better. On the 9th his pulse became soft, and he complained but little of head-ach. After appearing to be well for near three weeks, except that he complained of a little head-ach, on the 29th his pulse became again full and tense, for which I ordered him to lose six ounces of blood, which for the first time discovered a buffy coat. After this last bleeding, he discharged a large quantity of water. From this time he recovered slowly, but his pulse was a little fuller than natural on the 19th of January following. He afterwards enjoyed good health.

CASES III. AND IV.

In the month of March, 1792, I attended two children of three years of age, the one the daughter of William King, the other the daughter of William Blake: each of whom had most of the symptoms of the inflammatory stage of the internal dropsy of the brain. I prescribed the loss of four ounces of blood, and a smart purge in both cases, and in the course of a few days had the pleasure of observing all the symptoms of the disease perfectly subdued in each of them.

CASE V.

In the months of July and August, 1792, I attended a female slave of Mrs. Oneal, of St. Croix, who had an obstinate head-ach, coma, vomiting, and a tense, full, and *slow* pulse. I believed it to be the phrenicula, or internal dropsy of the brain, in its inflammatory stage. I bled her five times in the course of two months, and each time with obvious relief of all the symptoms of the disease. Finding that her head-ach, and a disposition to vomit, continued after the tension of her pulse was nearly reduced, I gave her as much calomel as excited a gentle salivation, which in a few weeks completed her cure.

CASE VI.

The daughter of Robert Moffat, aged eight years, in consequence of the suppression of a habitual discharge from sores on her head, in the month of April, 1793, was affected by violent head-ach, puking, great pains and weakness in her limbs, and a full, tense, and *slow* pulse. I believed these symptoms to be produced by an inflammation of the brain. I ordered her to lose six or seven ounces of blood, and gave her two purges of jalap and calomel, which operated very plentifully. I afterwards applied a blister to her neck. In one week from the time of my first visit to her she appeared to be in perfect health.

CASE VII.

A young woman of eighteen years of age, a hired servant in the family of Mrs. Elizabeth Smith, had been subject to a head-ach every spring for several years. The unusually warm days which occurred in the beginning of April, 1793, produced a return of this periodical pain. On the eighth of the month, it was so severe as to confine her to her bed. I was called to visit her on the ninth. I found her comatose, and, when awake, delirious. Her pupils were unusually dilated, and insensible to the light. She was constantly sick at her stomach, and vomited frequently. Her bowels were obstinately costive, and her pulse was full, tense, and so slow as seldom to exceed, for several days, from 56 to 60 strokes in a minute. I ordered her to lose ten ounces of blood every day, for three days successively, and gave her, on each of those days, strong doses of jalap and aloes. The last blood which was drawn from her was sizy. The purges procured from three to ten discharges every day from her bowels. On the 12th, she appeared to be much better. Her pulse was less tense, and beat 80 strokes in a minute. On the 14th, she had a fainting fit. On the 15th, she sat up, and called for food. The pupils of her eyes now recovered their sensibility to light, as well as their natural size. Her head-ach left her, and, on the 17th, she appeared to be in good health. Her pulse, however, continued to beat between 50 and 60 strokes in a minute, and retained a small portion of irregular action for several days after she recovered.

I am the more disposed to pronounce the cases which have been described to have been internal dropsy of the brain, from my having never been deceived in a single case in which I have examined the brains of patients whom I have suspected to have died of it.

I could add many other cases to those which have been related, but enough, I hope, have been mentioned to establish the safety and efficacy of the remedies that have been recommended.

I believe, with Dr. Quin, that this disease is much more frequent than is commonly supposed. I can recollect many cases of anomalous fever and head-ach in children, which have excited the most distressing apprehensions of an approaching internal dropsy of the brain, but which have yielded in a few days to bleeding, or to purges and blisters. I think it probable, that some, or perhaps most of these cases, might have terminated in an effusion of water in the brain, had they been left to themselves, or not been treated with the above remedies. I believe further, that it is often prevented by all those physicians who treat the first stage of febrile diseases in children with evacuations, just as the pulmonary consumption is prevented by bleeding, and low diet, in an inflammatory catarrh.

Where blood-letting has failed of curing this disease, I am disposed to ascribe it to its being used less copiously than the disease required. If its relation to pneumonicula be the same in its cure, that I have supposed it to be in its cause, then I am persuaded, that the same excess in blood-letting is indicated in it, above what is necessary in phrenitis, that has been practised in pneumonicula, above what is necessary in the cure of an acute inflammation of the lungs. The continuance, and, in some instances, the increase of the appetite in the internal dropsy of the brain, would seem to favour this opinion no less in this disease, than in the inflammatory state of pulmonary consumption. The extreme danger from the effusion of water into the ventricles of the brain, and the certainty of death from its confinement there, is a reason likewise why more blood should be drawn in this disease, than in diseases of the same force in other parts of the body, where the products of inflammation have a prompt, or certain outlet from the body. Where the internal dropsy is obviously the effect of a fall, or of any other cause which acts *directly* on the brain, there can be no doubt of the safety of very plentiful bleeding; all practical writers upon surgery concur in advising it. The late Dr. Pennington favoured me with an extract from Mr. Cline's manuscript lectures upon anatomy, delivered in London in the winter of 1792, which places the advantage of blood-letting, in that species of inflammation which follows a local injury of the brain, in a very strong point of light. "I know (says he) that several practitioners object to the use of evacuations as remedies for concussions of the brain, because of the weakness of the pulse; but in these cases the pulse is *depressed*. Besides, experience shows, that evacuations are frequently attended with very great advantages. I remember a remarkable case of a man in this [St. Thomas's] hospital, who was under the care of Mr. Baker. He lay in a comatose state for three weeks after an injury of the head. During that time he was bled *twenty* times, that is to say, he was bled once every day upon an average. He was bled twice a day *plentifully*, but towards the conclusion he was bled more sparingly, and only every other day; but at each bleeding, there were taken, upon an average, about sixteen ounces of blood. In consequence of this treatment, the man perfectly recovered his health and reason."

Local bleeding by cups, leaches, scarifications, or arteriotomy, should be combined with venesection, or preferred to it, where the whole arterial system does not sympathize with the disease in the brain.

II. A second remedy to be used in the second stage of this disease is *purges*. I have constantly observed all the patients whose cases have been related, to be relieved by plentiful and repeated evacuations from the bowels. I was led to the use of frequent purges, by having long observed their good effects in palsies, and other cases of congestion in the brain, where blood-letting was unsafe, and where it had been used without benefit. In the Leipsic Commentaries[56], there is an account of a case of internal dropsy of the brain, which followed the measles, being cured by no other medicines than purges and diuretics. I can say nothing in favour of the latter remedy, in this disease, from my own experience. The foxglove has been used in this city by several respectable practitioners, but, I believe, in no instance with any advantage.

III. *Blisters* have been uniformly recommended by all practical writers upon this disease. I have applied them to the head, neck, and temples, and generally with obvious relief to the pain in the head. They should be omitted in no stage of the disease; for even in its inflammatory stage, the discharge they occasion from the vessels of the head, greatly overbalances their stimulating effects upon the whole system.

IV. *Mercury* was long considered as the only remedy, which gave the least chance of a recovery from a dropsy of the brain. Out of all the cases in which I gave it, before the year 1790, I succeeded in but two: one of them was a child of three years old, the other was a young woman of twenty-six years of age. I am the more convinced that the latter case was internal dropsy of the brain, from my patient having relapsed, and died between two or three years afterwards, of the same disease. Since I have adopted the depleting remedies which have been mentioned, I have declined giving mercury altogether, except when combined with some purging medicine, and I have given it in this form chiefly with a view of dislodging worms. My reasons for not giving it as a sialagogue are the uncertainty of its operation, its frequent inefficacy when it excites a salivation, and, above all, its disposition to produce gangrene in the tender jaws of children. Seven instances of its inducing death from that cause, in children between three and eight years of age, and with circumstances of uncommon distress, have occurred in Philadelphia since the year 1795.

V. *Linen cloths*, wetted with cold vinegar, or water, and applied to the forehead, contribute very much to relieve the pain in the head. In the case of Mr. Cypher's son[57], the solution of ice in the vinegar appeared to afford the most obvious relief of this distressing symptom.

A puncture in the brain has been proposed by some writers to discharge the water from its ventricles. If the theory I have delivered be true, the operation promises nothing, even though it could always be performed with perfect safety. In cases of local injuries, or of inflammation from any cause, it must necessarily increase the disease; and in cases of effusion only, the debilitated state of the whole system forbids us to hope for any relief from such a local remedy.

Bark, wine, and opium promise much more success in the last stage of the disease. I can say nothing in their favour from my own experience; but from the aid they afford to mercury in other diseases, I conceive they might be made to accompany it with advantage.

Considering the nature of the indirect causes which induce the disease, and the case of a relapse, which has been mentioned, after an interval of near three years, as well as the symptoms of slow convalescence, manifested by the pulse, which occurred in the first and seventh cases, I submit it to the consideration of physicians, whether the use of moderate exercise, and the cold bath, should not be recommended to prevent a return of the disease in every case, where it has yielded to the power of medicine.

I have great pleasure in adding, that the theory of this disease, which I have delivered, has been adopted by many respectable physicians in Philadelphia, and in other parts of the United States, and that it has led to the practice that has been recommended, particularly to copious blood-letting; in consequence of which, death from a dropsy of the brain is not a more frequent occurrence, than from any other of the acute febrile diseases of our country.

Footnotes:

[46] Prælectiones, vol. I. p. 254.

[47] Historia Anatomica-Medica, vol. II.

[48] Treatise on the Infantile Remitting Fever.

[49] Medical Memoirs, vol. I. p. 174.

[50] Essays, Medical, Philosophical, and Experimental, vol. II. p. 339, 340.

[51] Historia Anatomica-Medica, vol. II. lib. tertius. obs. 380, 394, 1121.

[52] Obs. 383, 431.

[53] Medical Journal.

[54] Medical Memoirs, vol. I. p. 171.

[55] Medical Journal, vol. VIII.

[56] Vol. xxix. p. 139.

[57] Case II.

OBSERVATIONS
UPON
THE NATURE AND CURE
OF THE
GOUT.

In treating upon the gout, I shall deliver a few preliminary propositions.

1. The gout is a disease of the whole system. It affects the ligaments, blood-vessels, stomach, bowels, brain, liver, lymphatics, nerves, muscles, cartilages, bones, and skin.

2. The gout is a primary disease, only of the solids. Chalk-stones, abscesses, dropsical effusions into cavities, and cellular membrane, and eruptions on the skin, are all the effects of a morbid action in the blood-vessels. The truth of this proposition has been ably proved by Dr. Cullen in his First Lines.

3. It affects most frequently persons of a sanguineous temperament; but sometimes it affects persons of nervous and phlegmatic temperaments. The idle and luxurious are more subject to it, than the labouring and temperate part of mankind. Women are said to be less subject to it than men. I once believed, and taught this opinion, but I now retract it. From the peculiar delicacy of the female constitution, and from the thin covering they wear on their feet and limbs, the gout is less apt to fall upon those parts than in men, but they exhibit all its other symptoms, perhaps more frequently than men, in other parts of the body. The remote causes of gout moreover to be mentioned presently, act with equal force upon both sexes, and more of them I believe upon women, than upon men.

It generally attacks in those periods of life, and in those countries, and seasons of the year, in which inflammatory diseases are most common. It seldom affects persons before puberty, or in old age, and yet I have heard of its appearing with all its most characteristic symptoms in this city in a child of 6, and in a man above 80 years of age. Men of active minds are said to be most subject to it, but I think I have seen it as frequently in persons of slender and torpid intellects, as in persons of an opposite character. I have heard of a case of gout in an Indian at Pittsburg, and I have cured a fit of it in an Indian in this city. They had both been intemperate in the use of wine and fermented liquors.

4. It is in one respect a hereditary disease, depending upon the propagation of a similar temperament from father to son. When a predisposition to the gout has been derived from ancestors, less force in exciting causes will induce it than in those habits where this has not been the case. This predisposition sometimes passes by children, and appears in grand-children. There are instances likewise in which it has passed by the males, and appeared only in the females of a family. It even appears in the descendants of families who have been reduced to poverty, but not often where they have been obliged to labour for a subsistence. It generally passes by those children who are born before the gout makes its appearance in a father. It is curious to observe how extensively the predisposition pervades some families. An English gentleman, who had been afflicted with the gout, married a young woman in Philadelphia many years ago, by whom he had one daughter. His wife dying three weeks after the birth of this child, he returned to England, where he married a second wife, by whom he had six children, all of whom except one died with the gout before they attained to the usual age of matrimony in Great Britain. One of them died in her 16th year. Finally the father and grandfather died with the same disease. The daughter whom this afflicted gentleman left in this city, passed her life subject to the gout, and finally died under my care in the year 1789, in the 68th year of her age. She left a family of children, two of whom had the gout. One of them, a lady, has suffered exquisitely from it.

5. The gout is always induced by general predisposing debility.

6. The remote causes of the gout which induce this debility, are, indolence, great bodily labour, long protracted bodily exercise, intemperance in eating, and in venery, acid aliments and drinks, strong tea and coffee, public and domestic vexation, the violent, or long continued exercise of the understanding, imagination, and passions in study, business, or pleasure, and, lastly, the use of ardent, and fermented liquors. The last are absolutely necessary to produce that form of gout which appears in the ligaments and muscles. I assert this, not only from my own observations, but from those of Dr. Cadogan, and Dr. Darwin, who say they never saw a case of gout in the limbs in any person who had not used spirits or wine in a greater or less quantity. Perhaps this may be another reason why women, who drink less of those liquors than men, are so rarely affected with this disease in the extreme parts of their bodies. Wines of all kinds are more disposed to produce this form of gout than spirits. The reason of this must be resolved into the less stimulus in the former, than in the latter liquors. Wine appears to resemble, in its action upon the body, the moderate stimulus of miasmata which produce a common remitting fever, or intermitting fever, while spirits resemble that violent action induced by miasmata which passes by the blood-vessels, ligaments, and muscles, and invades at once the liver, bowels, and

brain. There is one symptom of the gout in the extremities which seems to be produced exclusively by ardent spirits, and that is a burning in the palms of the hands, and soles of the feet. This is so uniform, that I have sometimes been able to convict my patients of intemperance in the use of spirits, when no other mark of their having taken them in *excess*, appeared in the system.

I have enumerated among the remote causes of the gout, the use of strong tea. I infer its predisposing quality to that disease, from its frequency at Japan, where tea is used in large quantities, and from the gout being more common among that sex in our country who drink the most, and the strongest tea.

7. The exciting causes of the gout are frequently a greater degree, or a sudden application of its remote and predisposing causes. They act upon the accumulated excitability of the system, and by destroying its equilibrium of excitement, and regular order of actions, produce convulsion, or irregular morbid and local excitement. These exciting causes are either of a stimulating, or of a sedative nature. The former are violent exercise, of body or mind, night-watching, and even sitting up late at night, a hearty meal, a fit of drunkenness, a few glasses of claret or a draught of cyder, where those liquors have not been habitual to the patient, a sudden paroxysm of joy, anger, or terror, a dislocation of a bone, straining of a joint, particularly of the ankle, undue pressure upon the foot, or leg, from a tight shoe or boot, an irritated corn, and the usual remote causes of fever. The latter exciting causes are sudden inanition from bleeding, purging, vomiting, fasting, cold, a sudden stoppage of moisture on the feet, fear, grief, excess in venery, and the debility left upon the system by the crisis of a fever. All these causes act more certainly when they are aided by the additional debility induced upon the system in sleep. It is for this reason that the gout generally makes its first attack in the night, and in a part of the system most remote from the energy of the brain, and most debilitated by exercise, viz. in the great toe, or in some part of the foot. In ascribing a fit of the gout to a cause which is of a sedative nature, the reader will not suppose that I have departed from the simplicity and uniformity of a proposition I have elsewhere delivered, that disease is the effect of stimulus. The abstraction of a natural and habitual impression of any kind, by increasing the force of those which remain, renders the production of morbid and excessive actions in the system as much the effect of preternatural or disproportioned stimulus, as if they were induced by causes that are externally and evidently stimulating. It is thus in many other of the operations of nature, opposite causes produce the same effects.

8. The gout consists simply in morbid excitement, accompanied with irregular action, or the absence of all action from the force of stimulus. There is nothing specific in the morbid excitement and actions which take place in the gout different from what occur in fevers. It is to be lamented that a kind of metastasis of error has taken place in pathology. The rejection of a specific

acrimony as the cause of each disease, has unfortunately been followed by a belief in as many specific actions as there are different forms and grades of disease, and thus perpetuated the evils of our ancient systems of medicine. However varied morbid actions may be by their causes, seats, and effects, they are all of the same nature, and the time will probably come when the whole nomenclature of morbid actions will be absorbed in the single name of disease.

I shall now briefly enumerate the symptoms of the gout, as they appear in the ligaments, the blood-vessels, the viscera, the nervous system, the alimentary canal, the lymphatics, the skin, and the bones of the human body, and here we shall find that it is an epitome of all disease.

I. The ligaments which connect the bones are the seats, of what is called a legitimate or true gout. They are affected with pain, swelling, and inflammation. The pain is sometimes so acute as to be compared to the gnawing of a dog. We perceive here the sameness of the gout with the rheumatism. Many pages, and indeed whole essays, have been composed by writers to distinguish them, but they are exactly the same disease while the morbid actions are confined to this part of the body. They are, it is true, produced by different remote causes, but this constitutes no more difference in their nature, than is produced in a coal of fire, whether it be inflamed by a candle, or by a spark of electricity. The morbid actions which are induced by the usual causes of rheumatism affect, though less frequently, the lungs, the trachea, the head, the bowels, and even the heart, as well as the gout. Those actions, moreover, are the means of a fluid being effused, which is changed into calcareous matter in the joints and other parts of the body, exactly like that which is produced by the gout. They likewise twist and dislocate the bones in common with the gout, in a manner to be described hereafter. The only difference between what are called gouty, and rheumatic actions, consists in their seats, and in the degrees of their force. The debility which predisposes to the gout, being greater, and more extensively diffused through the body than the debility which precedes rheumatism, the morbid actions, in the former case, pass more readily from external to internal parts, and produce in both more acute and more dangerous effects. A simile derived from the difference in the degrees of action produced in the system by marsh miasmata, made use of upon a former occasion, will serve me again to illustrate this part of our subject. A mild remittent, and a yellow fever, are different grades of the same disease. The former, like the rheumatism, affects the bones chiefly with pain, while the latter, like the gout, affects not only the bones, but the stomach, bowels, brain, nerves, lymphatics, and all the internal parts of the body.

II. In the arterial system the gout produces fever. This fever appears not only in the increased force or frequency of the pulse, but in morbid affections of all the viscera. It puts on all the different grades of fever, from the malignity of the plague, to the mildness of a common intermittent. It has moreover its regular exacerbations and remissions once in every four and twenty hours, and its crisis usually on the fourteenth day, in violent cases. In moderate attacks, it runs on from twenty to forty days in common with the typhus or slow chronic state of fever. It is common for those persons who consider the gout as a specific disease, when it appears in the above forms, to say, that it is complicated with fever; but this is an error, for there can exist but one morbid action in the blood-vessels at once, and the same laws are imposed upon the morbid actions excited in those parts of the body by the remote causes of the gout, as by the common causes of fever. I have seen two instances of this disease appearing in the form of a genuine hectic, and one in which it appeared to yield to lunar influence, in the manner described by Dr. Balfour. In the highly inflammatory state of the gout, the sensibility of the blood-vessels far exceeds what is seen in the same state of fever from more common causes. I have known an instance in which a translation of the gouty action to the eye produced such an exquisite degree of sensibility, that the patient was unable to bear the feeble light which was emitted from a few coals of fire in his room, at a time too when the coldness of the weather would have made a large fire agreeable to him. It is from the extreme sensibility which the gout imparts to the stomach, that the bark is so generally rejected by it. I knew a British officer who had nearly died from taking a spoonful of the infusion of that medicine, while his arterial system was in this state of morbid excitability, from a fit of the gout. It is remarkable that the gout is most disposed to assume a malignant character, during the prevalence of an inflammatory constitution of the atmosphere. This has been long ago remarked by Dr. Huxham. Several instances of it have occurred in this city since the year 1793.

III. The gout affects most of the viscera. In the brain it produces head-ach, vertigo, coma, apoplexy, and palsy. In the lungs it produces pneumonia vera, notha, asthma, hæmoptysis, pulmonary consumption, and a short hecking cough, first described by Dr. Sydenham. In the throat it produces inflammatory angina. In the uterus it produces hæmorrhagia uterina. It affects the kidneys with inflammation, strangury, diabetes, and calculi. The position of the body for weeks or months on the back, by favouring the compression of the kidneys by the bowels, is the principal reason why those parts suffer so much in gouty people. The strangury appears to be produced by the same kind of engorgement or choking of the vessels of the kidneys, which takes place in the small-pox and yellow fever. Four cases of it are described in the 3d volume of the Physical and Literary Essays of Edinburgh, by Dr. David Clerk. I have seen one instance of death in an old man from this cause. The catheter brought no water from his bladder. The late Mr. John Penn, formerly governor of Pennsylvania, I have been informed by one of his physicians, died from a similar affection in his kidneys from gout. The catheter was as ineffectual in giving him relief, as it was in the case of my patient. The neck of the bladder sometimes becomes the seat of the gout. It discovers itself by spasm, and a suppression of urine in some cases, and occasionally by a habitual discharge of mucus through the urethra. This disease has been called, by Lieutaud, "a catarrh of the bladder." Dr. Stoll describes it, and calls it "hæmorrhoids of the bladder." But of all the viscera, the liver suffers most from the gout. It produces in it inflammation, suppuration, melena, schirrus, gall-stones, jaundice, and a habitual increased secretion and excretion of bile. These affections of the liver appear most frequently in southern countries, and in female habits. They are substitutes for a gout in the ligaments, and in the extremities of the body. They appear likewise in drunkards from ardent spirits. It would seem that certain stimuli act specifically upon the liver, probably for the wise purpose of discharging such parts of the blood from the body, as are vitiated by the rapidity of its circulation. I shall, in another place[58], take notice of the action of marsh miasmata upon the livers of men and beasts. It has been observed that hogs that live near brewhouses, and feed upon the fermented grains of barley, always discover enlarged or diseased livers. But a determination of the blood to the liver, and an increased action of its vessels, are produced by other causes than marsh miasmata, and fermented and distilled liquors. They appear in the fever which accompanies madness and the malignant sore-throat, also in contusions of the brain, and in the excited state of the blood-vessels which is produced by anger and exercise. I have found an attention to these facts useful in prescribing for diseases of the liver, inasmuch as they have led me from considering them as idiopathic affections, but as the effects only of morbid actions excited in other parts of the body.

IV. The gout sometimes affects the arterial and nervous systems *jointly*, producing in the brain, coma, vertigo, apoplexy, palsy, loss of memory, and madness, and in the *nerves*, hysteria, hypochondriasis, and syncope. It is common to say the gout counterfeits all these diseases. But this is an inaccurate mode of speaking. All those diseases have but one cause, and they are exactly the same, however different the stimulus may be, from which they are derived. Sometimes the gout affects the brain and nerves exclusively, without producing the least morbid action in the blood-vessels. I once attended a gentleman from Barbadoes who suffered, from this affection of his brain and nerves, the most intolerable depression of spirits. It yielded to large doses of wine, but his relief was perfect, and more durable, when a pain was excited by nature or art, in his hands or feet.

The muscles are sometimes affected by the gout with spasm, with general and partial convulsions, and lastly with great pain. Dr. Stoll describes a case of opisthotonos from it. The angina pectoris, or a sudden inability to breathe after climbing a hill, or a pair of stairs, and after a long walk, is sometimes a symptom of the gout. There is a pain which suddenly pervades the head, breast, and limbs, which resembles an electric shock. I have known two instances of it in gouty patients, and have taken the liberty of calling it the "aura arthritica." But the pain which affects the muscles is often of a more permanent nature. It is felt with most severity in the calves of the legs. Sometimes it affects the muscles of the head, breast, and limbs, exciting in them large and distressing swellings. But further; the gout in some cases seizes upon the tendons, and twists them in such a manner as to dislocate bones in the hands and feet. It even affects the cartilages. Of this I once saw an instance in colonel Adams, of the state of Maryland. The external parts of both his ears were so much inflamed in a fit of the gout, that he was unable to lie on either of his sides.

V. The gout affects the alimentary canal, from the stomach to its termination in the rectum. Flatulency, sickness, acidity, indigestion, pain, or vomiting, usually usher in a fit of the disease. The sick head-ach, also dyspepsia, with all its train of distressing evils, are frequently the effects of gout concentrated in the stomach. I have seen a case in which the gout, by retreating to this viscus, produced the same burning sensation which is felt in the yellow fever. The patient who was the subject of this symptom died two days afterwards with a black vomiting. It was Mr. Patterson, formerly collector of the port of Philadelphia, under the British government. I was not surprised at these two uncommon symptoms in the gout, for I had long been familiar with its disposition to affect the biliary secretion, and the actions of the stomach. The colic and dysentery are often produced by the gout in the bowels. In the southern states of America, it sometimes produces a chronic diarrhœa, which is known in some places by the name of the "downward consumption." The piles are a common symptom of gout, and where they pour forth blood occasionally, render it a harmless disease. I have known an instance in which a gouty pain in the rectum produced involuntary stools in a gentleman in this city, and I have heard from a southern gentleman, who had been afflicted with gouty symptoms, that a similar pain was excited in the same part to such a degree, whenever he went into a crowded room lighted by candles, as to oblige him to leave it. In considering the effects of the gout upon this part, I am led to take notice of a troublesome itching in the anus which has been described by Dr. Lettsom, and justly attributed by him to this disease[59]. I have known several cases of it. They always occurred in gouty habits. A distressing collection of air in the rectum, which renders frequent retirement from company necessary to discharge it, is likewise a symptom of gout. It is accompanied with frequent, and small, but hard stools.

Of the above morbid affections of the nerves, stomach, and bowels, the hysteria, the sick head-ach, and the colic, appear much oftener in women than in men. I have said that dyspepsia is a symptom of gout. Out of more than 500 persons who were the patients of the Liverpool infirmary and dispensary, in one year, Dr. Currie informs us, "a great majority were females[60]."

VI. The gout affects the glands and lymphatics. It produced a salivation of a profuse nature in major Pearce Butler, which continued for two days. It produced a bubo in the groin in a citizen of Philadelphia. He had never been infected with the venereal disease, of course no suspicion was entertained by me of its being derived from that cause. I knew a lady who had periodical swellings in her breasts, at the same season of the year in which she had before been accustomed to have a regular fit of the gout. The scrophula and all the forms of dropsy are the effects in many cases of the disposition of the gout to attack the lymphatic system. There is a large hard swelling without pain, of one, or both the legs and thighs, which has been called a dropsy, but is very different from the common disease of that name. It comes on, and goes off suddenly. It has lately been called in England the *dumb* gout. In the spring of 1798 I attended colonel Innes, of Virginia, in consultation with my Edinburgh friend and fellow-student, Dr. Walter Jones, of the same state. The colonel had large anasarcous swellings in his thighs and legs, which we had reason to believe were the effects of an indolent gout. We made several punctures in his feet and ancles, and thereby discharged a large quantity of water from his legs and thighs. A day or two afterwards his ancles exhibited in pain and inflammation, the usual form of gout in those parts. In the year 1794 I attended Mrs. Lloyd Jones, who had a swelling of the same kind in her foot and leg. Her constitution, habits, and the sober manners of her ancestors, gave me no reason to suspect it to arise from the usual remote causes of gout. She was feverish, and her pulse was tense. I drew ten ounces of blood from her, and gave her a purge. The swelling subsided, but it was succeeded by an acute rheumatic pain in the part, which was cured in a few days. I mention these facts as an additional proof of the sameness of the gout and rheumatism, and to show that the vessels in a simple disease, as well as in malignant fevers, are often oppressed beyond that point in which they emit the sensation of pain.

Under this head I shall include an account of the mucous discharge from the urethra, which sometimes takes place in an attack of the gout, and which has ignorantly been ascribed to a venereal gonorrhæa. There is a description of this symptom of the gout in the 3d volume of the Physical and Literary Essays of Edinburgh, by Dr. Clark. It was first taken notice of by Sauvages by the name of "gonorrhæa podagrica," in a work entitled Pathologia Methodica. I have known three instances of it in this city. In the visits which the gout pays to the genitals, it sometimes excites great pain in the testicles. Dr. Whytt mentions three cases of this kind. One of them was attended with a troublesome itching of the scrotum. I have seen one case in which the testicles were affected with great pain, and the penis with an obstinate priapism. They succeeded a sudden translation of the gout from the bowels.

From the occasional disposition of the gout to produce a mucous discharge from the urethra in men, it is easy to conceive that it is the frequent cause of the fluor albus in women, for in them, the gout which is restrained from the feet, by a cause formerly mentioned, is driven to other parts, and particularly to that part which, from its offices, is more disposed to invite disease to it, than any other. The fluor albus sometimes occurs in females, apparently of the most robust habits. In such persons, more especially if they have been descended from gouty ancestors, and have led indolent and luxurious lives, there can be no doubt but the disease is derived from the gout, and should be treated with remedies which act not only upon the affected part, but the whole system. An itching similar to that I formerly mentioned in the anus, sometimes occurs in the vagina of women. Dr. Lettsom has described it. In all the cases I have known of it, I believe it was derived from the usual causes of the gout.

VII. There are many records in the annals of medicine of the gout affecting the skin. The erysipelas, gangrene, and petechiæ are its acute, and tetters, and running sores are its usual chronic forms when it appears in this part of the body. I attended a patient with the late Dr. Hutchinson, in whom the whole calf of one leg was destroyed by a mortification which succeeded the gout. Dr. Alexander, of Baltimore, informed me that petechiæ were among the last symptoms of this disease in the Rev. Mr. Oliver, who died in the town of Baltimore, about two years ago. In the disposition of the gout to attack external parts, it sometimes affects the eyes and ears with the most acute and distressing inflammation and pain. I hesitate the less in ascribing them both to the gout, because they not only occur in gouty habits, but because they now and then effuse a calcareous matter of the same nature with that which is found in the ligaments of the joints.

VIII. Even the bones are not exempted from the ravages of this disease. I have before mentioned that the bones of the hands and feet are sometimes dislocated by it. I have heard of an instance in which it dislocated the thigh bone. It probably produced this effect by the effusion of that part of the blood which constitutes chalk-stones, or by an excrescence of flesh in the cavity of the joint. Two instances have occurred in this city of its dislodging the teeth, after having produced the most distressing pains in the jaws. The long protracted, and acute pain in the face, which has been so accurately described by Dr. Fothergill, probably arises wholly from the gout acting upon the bones of the part affected.

I have more than once hinted at the sameness of some of the states of the gout, and the yellow fever. Who can compare the symptoms and seats of both diseases, and not admit the unity of the remote and immediate causes of fever?

Thus have I enumerated proofs of the gout being a disease of the *whole* system. I have only to add under this proposition, that it affects different parts of the body in different people, according to the nature of their congenital or acquired temperaments, and that it often passes from one part of the body to another in the twinkling of an eye.

The morbid excitement, and actions of the gout, when seated in the ligaments, the blood-vessels, and viscera, and left to themselves, produce effects different in their nature, according to the parts in which they take place. In the viscera they produce congestions composed of all the component parts of the blood. From the blood-vessels which terminate in hollow cavities and in cellular membrane, they produce those effusions of serum which compose dropsies. From the same vessels proceed those effusions which produce on the skin erysipelas, tetters, and all the different kinds of eruptions. In the ligaments they produce an effusion of coagulable lymph, which by stagnation is changed into what are called chalk-stones. In the urinary organs they produce an effusion of particles of coagulable lymph or red blood, which, under certain circumstances, are changed into sand, gravel, and stone. All these observations are liable to some exceptions. There are instances in which chalk-stones have been found in the lungs, mouth, on the eye-lids, and in the passages of the ears, and a preternatural flux of water and blood has taken place from the kidneys. Pus has likewise been formed in the joints, and air has been found in the cavity of the belly, instead of water.

Sometimes the gout is said to combine with the fevers which arise from cold and miasmata. We are not to suppose from this circumstance, that the system is under a twofold stimulus. By no means. The symptoms which are ascribed to the gout, are the effects of morbid excitement excited by the cold, or miasmata acting upon parts previously debilitated by the usual remote causes of that disease.

A bilious diathesis in the air so often excites the peculiar symptoms of gout, in persons predisposed to it, that it has sometimes been said to be epidemic. This was the case, Dr. Stoll says, in Vienna, in the years 1782 and 1784. The same mixture of gouty and bilious symptoms was observed by Dr. Hillary, in the fevers of Barbadoes.

From a review of the symptoms of the gout, the impropriety of distinguishing it from its various seats, by specific names, must be obvious to the reader. As well might we talk of a yellow fever in the brain, in the nerves, or in the groin, when its symptoms affect those parts, as talk of *misplaced* or *retrocedent* gout. The great toe, and the joints of the hands and feet, are no more its exclusive seats, than the "stomach is the throne of the yellow fever." In short, the gout may be compared to a monarch whose empire is unlimited. The whole body crouches before it.

It has been said as a reflection upon our profession, that physicians are always changing their opinions respecting chronic diseases. For a long while they were all classed under the heads of nervous, or bilious. These names for many years afforded a sanctuary for the protection of fraud and error in medicine. They have happily yielded of late years to the name of gout. If we mean by this disease a primary affection of the joints, we have gained nothing by assuming that name; but if we mean by it a disease which consists simply of morbid excitement, invited by debility, and disposed to invade every part of the body, we conform our ideas to facts, and thus simplify theory and practice in chronic diseases.

I proceed now to treat of the METHOD OF CURE.

Let not the reader startle when I mention curing the gout. It is not a sacred disease. There will be no profanity in handling it freely. It has been cured often, and I hope to deliver such directions under this head, as will reduce it as much under the power of medicine, as a pleurisy or an intermitting fever. Let not superstition say here, that the gout is the just punishment of folly, and vice, and that the justice of Heaven would be defeated by curing it. The venereal disease is more egregiously the effect of vice than the gout, and yet Heaven has kindly directed human reason to the discovery of a remedy which effectually eradicates it from the constitution. This opinion of the gout being a curable disease, is as humane as it is just. It is calculated to prompt to early application for medical aid, and to prevent that despair of relief which has contributed so much to its duration, and mortality.

But does not the gout prevent other diseases, and is it not improper upon this account to cure it? I answer, that it prevents other diseases, as the daily use of drams prevents the intermitting fever. In doing this, they bring on a hundred more incurable morbid affections. The yellow fever carried off many chronic diseases in the year 1793, and yet who would wish for, or admit such a remedy for a similar purpose? The practice of encouraging, and inviting what has been called a "friendly fit" of the gout as a cure for other diseases, resembles the practice of school boys who swallow the stones of cherries to assist their stomachs in digesting that delicate fruit. It is no more necessary to produce the gout in the feet, in order to cure it, than it is to wait for, or encourage abscesses or natural hæmorrhages, to cure a fever. The practice originated at a time when morbific matter was supposed to be the cause of the gout, but it has unfortunately continued under the influence of theories which have placed the seat of the disease in the solids.

The remedies for the gout naturally divide themselves into the following heads.

I. Such as are proper in its approaching, or forming state.

II. Such as are proper in *violent* morbid action in the blood-vessels and viscera.

III. Such as are proper in a *feeble* morbid action in the same parts of the body.

IV. Such as are proper to relieve certain local symptoms which are not accompanied by general morbid action. And

V. Such as are proper to prevent its recurrence, or, in other words, to eradicate it from the system.

I. The symptoms of an approaching fit of the gout are great languor, and dulness of body and mind, doziness, giddiness, wakefulness, or sleep disturbed by vivid dreams, a dryness, and sometimes a coldness, numbness, and prickling in the feet and legs, a disappearance of pimples in the face, occasional chills, acidity and flatulency in the stomach, with an increased, a weak, or a defect of appetite. These symptoms are not universal, but more or less of them usher in nearly every fit of the gout. The reader will see at once their sameness with the premonitory symptoms of fever from cold and miasmata, and assent from this proof, in addition to others formerly mentioned, to the propriety of considering a fit of the gout, as a paroxysm of fever.

The system, during the existence of these symptoms, is in a state of morbid depression. The disease is as yet unformed, and may easily be prevented by the loss of a few ounces of blood, or, if this remedy be objected to, by a gentle doze of physic, and afterwards by bathing the feet in warm water, by a few drops of the spirit of hartshorn in a little sage or camomile tea, by a draught of wine whey, or a common doze of liquid laudanum, and, according to a late Portuguese physician, by taking a few doses of bark.

It is worthy of notice, that if these remedies are omitted, all the premonitory symptoms that have been mentioned disappear as soon as the arthritic fever is formed, just as lassitude and chilliness yield to a paroxysm of fever from other causes.

II. Of the remedies that are proper in cases of great morbid action in the blood-vessels and viscera.

I shall begin this head by repudiating the notion of a specific cure for the gout existing in any single article of the materia medica. Every attempt to cure it by elixirs, diet-drinks, pills, or boluses, which were intended to act singly on the system, has been as unsuccessful as the attempts to cure the whooping cough by spells, or tricks of legerdemain.

The first remedy that I shall mention for reducing great morbid action in the blood-vessels and viscera, is *blood-letting*. I was first taught the safety of this remedy in the gout by reading the works of Dr. Lister, above thirty years ago, and I have used it ever since with great advantage. It has the sanction of Dr. Hoffman, Dr. Cullen, and many others of the first names in medicine in its favour.

The usual objections to bleeding as a remedy, have been urged with more success in the gout, than in any other disease. It has been forbidden, because the gout is said to be a disease of debility. This is an error. Debility is not a disease. It is only its predisposing cause. Disease is preternatural strength in the state of the system now under consideration, occasioned by the abstraction of excitement from one part, and the accumulation of it in another part of the body. Every argument in favour of bleeding in a pleurisy applies in the present instance, for they both depend upon the same kind of morbid action in the blood-vessels. Bleeding acts moreover alike in both cases by abstracting the excess of excitement from the blood-vessels, and restoring its natural and healthy equality to every part of the system.

It has been further said, that bleeding disposes to more frequent returns of the gout. This objection to the lancet has been urged by Dr. Sydenham, who was misled in his opinion of it, by his theory of the disease being the offspring of morbific matter. The assertion is unfounded, for bleeding in a fit of the gout has no such effect, provided the remedies to be mentioned hereafter are used to prevent it. But a fit of the gout is not singular in its disposition to recur after being once cured. The rheumatism, the pleurisy, and the intermitting fever are all equally disposed to return when persons are exposed to their remote and exciting causes, and yet we do not upon this account consider them as incurable diseases, nor do we abstain from the usual remedies which cure them.

The inflammatory or violent state of the gout is said most commonly to affect the limbs. But this is far from being the case. It frequently makes its first attack upon the head, lungs, kidneys, stomach, and bowels. The remedies for expelling it from the stomach and bowels are generally of a stimulating nature. They are as improper in full habits, and in the recent state of the disease, as cordials are to drive the small-pox from the vitals to the skin. Hundreds have been destroyed by them. Bleeding in these cases affords the same speedy and certain relief that it does in removing pain from the stomach and bowels in the first stage of the yellow fever. Colonel Miles owes his life to the loss of 60 ounces of blood in an attack of the gout in his bowels, in the winter of 1795, and major Butler derived the same benefit from the loss of near 30 ounces, in an attack of the gout in his stomach in the spring of 1798.

I could add many more instances of the efficacy of the lancet in the gout when it affects the viscera, from my own experience, but I prefer mentioning one only from sir John Floyer, which is more striking than any I have met with in its favour. He tells us, sir Henry Coningsby was much disposed to the palsy from the gout when he was 30 years old. By frequent bleedings, and the use of the cold bath, he recovered, and lived to be 88. During his old age, he was bled every three months.

I have said, in the history of the symptoms of the gout, that it sometimes appeared in the form of a hectic fever. I have prescribed occasional bleedings in a case of this kind accompanied with a tense pulse, with the happiest effects. It confined the disease for several years wholly to the blood-vessels, and it bid fair in time to eradicate it from the system.

The state of the pulse, as described in another place[61], should govern the use of the lancet in this disease. Bleeding is required as much in its depressed, as in its full and chorded state. Colonel Miles's pulse, at the time he suffered from the gout in his bowels, was scarcely perceptible. It did not rise till after a second or third bleeding.

Some advantage may be derived from examining the blood. I have once known it to be dissolved; but for the most part I have observed it, with Dr. Lister, to be covered with the buffy coat of common inflammation.

The arguments made use of in favour of bleeding in the diseases of old people in a former volume, apply with equal force to its use in the gout. The inflammatory state of this disease frequently occurs in the decline of life, and bleeding is as much indicated in such cases as in any other inflammatory fever. The late Dr. Chovet died with an inflammation in his liver from gout, in the 86th year of his age. He was twice bled, and his blood each time was covered with a buffy coat.

Where the gout affects the head with obstinate pain, and appears to be seated in the muscles, cupping and leeches give great relief. This mode of bleeding should be trusted in those cases only in which the morbid action is confined chiefly to the head, and appears in a feeble state in the rest of the arterial system.

The advantages of bleeding in the gout, when performed under all the circumstances that have been mentioned, are as follow:

1. It removes or lessens pain.

2. It prevents those congestions and effusions which produce apoplexy, palsy, pneumonia notha, calculi in the kidneys and bladder, and chalk-stones in the hands and feet. The gravel and stone are nine times in ten, I believe, the effects of an effusion of lymph or blood from previous morbid action in the kidneys. If this disease were narrowly watched, and cured as often as it occurs, by the loss of blood, we should have but little gravel or stone among gouty people. A citizen of Philadelphia died a few years ago, in the 96th year of his age, who had been subject to the strangury the greatest part of his life. His only remedy for it was bleeding. He lived free from the gravel and stone; and died, or rather appeared to fall asleep in death, from old age. Dr. Haller mentions a similar case in his Bibliotheca Medicinæ, in which bleeding had the same happy effects.

3. It prevents the system from wearing itself down by fruitless pain and sickness, and thereby inducing a predisposition to frequent returns of the disease.

4. It shortens the duration of a fit of gout, by throwing it, not into the feet, but out of the system, and thus prevents a patient's lying upon his back for two or three months with a writhing face, scolding a wife and family of children, and sometimes cursing every servant that comes near enough to endanger the touch of an inflamed limb. Besides preventing all this parade of pain and peevishness, it frequently, when assisted with other remedies to be mentioned presently, restores a man to his business and society in two or three days: a circumstance this of great importance in the public as well as private pursuits of men; for who has not read of the most interesting affairs of nations being neglected or protracted, by the principal agents in them being suddenly confined to their beds, or chairs, for weeks or months, by a fit of the gout?

2. A second remedy in the state of the gout which has been mentioned, is *purging.* Sulphur is generally preferred for this purpose, but castor oil, cream of tartar, sena, jalap, rhubarb, and calomel, may all be used with equal safety and advantage. The stomach and habits of the patient should determine the choice of a suitable purge in every case. Salts are generally offensive to the stomach. They once brought on a fit of the gout in Dr. Brown.

3. *Vomits* may be given in all those cases where bleeding is objected to, or where the pulse is only moderately active. Mr. Small, in an excellent paper

upon the gout, in the 6th volume of the Medical Observations and Inquiries, p. 205, containing the history of his own case, tells us that he always took a vomit upon the first attack of the gout, and that it never failed of relieving all its symptoms. The matter discharged by this vomit indicated a morbid state of the liver, for it was always a dark greenish bile, which was insoluble in water. A British lieutenant, whose misfortunes reduced him to the necessity of accepting a bed in the poor-house of this city, informed the late Dr. Stuben, that he had once been much afflicted with the gout, and that he had upon many occasions strangled a fit of it by the early use of an emetic. Dr. Pye adds his testimony to those which have been given in favour of vomits, and says further, that they do most service when they discharge an acid humour from the stomach. They appear to act in part by equalizing the divided excitement of the system, and in part by discharging the contents of the gall-bladder and stomach, vitiated by the previous debility of those organs. Care should be taken not to exhibit this remedy where the gout attacks the stomach with symptoms of inflammation, or where it has a tendency to fix itself upon the brain.

4. *Nitre* may be given with advantage in cases of inflammatory action, where the stomach is not affected.

5. A fifth remedy is *cool* or *cold air*. This is as safe and useful in the gout as in any other inflammatory state of fever. The affected limbs should be kept out of bed, *uncovered*. In this way Mr. Small says he moderated the pains of the gout in his hands and feet[62]. I have directed the same practice with great comfort, as well as advantage to my patients. Even cold water has been applied with good effects to a limb inflamed by the gout. Mr. Blair M'Clenachan taught me the safety and benefit of this remedy, by using it upon himself without the advice of a physician. It instantly removed his pain, nor was the gout translated by it to any other part of his body. It was removed in the same manner, Dr. Heberden tells us, by the celebrated Dr Harvey from his own feet. Perhaps it would be best in most cases to prefer cool, or cold air, to cold water. The safety and advantages of both these modes of applying cold to the affected limbs, show the impropriety of the common practice of wrapping them in flannel.

6. *Diluting liquors*, such as are prescribed in common inflammatory fevers, should be given in such quantities as to dispose to a gentle perspiration.

7. *Abstinence from wine, spirits, and malt liquors*, also from such aliments as afford much nourishment or stimulus, should be carefully enjoined. Sago, panada, tapioca, diluted milk with bread, and the pulp of apples, summer fruits, tea, coffee, weak chocolate, and bread soaked in chicken water or beef tea, should constitute the principal diet of patients in this state of the gout.

8. *Blisters* are an invaluable remedy in this disease, when used at a proper time, that is, after the reduction of the morbid actions in the system by evacuations. They should be applied to the joints of the feet and wrists in general gout, and to the neck and sides, when it attacks the head or breast. A strangury from the gout is no objection to their use. So far from increasing this complaint, Dr. Clark and Dr. Whytt inform us, that they remove it[63]. But the principal advantage of blisters is derived from their collecting and concentrating scattered and painful sensations, and conveying them out of the system, and thus becoming excellent substitutes for a tedious fit of the gout.

9. *Fear* and *terror* have in some instances cured a paroxysm of this disease. A captain of a British ship of war, who had been confined for several weeks to his cabin, by a severe fit of the gout in his feet, was suddenly cured by hearing the cry of fire on board his ship. This fact was communicated to me by a gentleman who was a witness of it. Many similar cases are upon record in books of medicine. I shall in another place insert an account of one in which the cure effected by a fright, eradicated the disease from the system so completely, as ever afterwards to prevent its return.

Thus have I enumerated the remedies which are proper in the gout when it affects the blood-vessels and viscera with great morbid action. Most of those remedies are alike proper when the morbid actions are seated in the muscular fibres, whether of the bowels or limbs, and whether they produce local pain, or general convulsion, provided they are of a violent nature.

There are some remedies under this head of a doubtful nature, on which I shall make a few observations.

Sweating has been recommended in this state of the gout. All the objections to it in preference to other modes of depletion, mentioned in another place[64], apply against its use in the inflammatory state of the gout. It is not only less safe than bleeding, purging, and abstinence, but it is often an impracticable remedy. The only sudorific medicine to be trusted in this state of the disease is the Seneka snake-root. It promotes all the secretions and excretions, and exerts but a feeble stimulus upon the arterial system.

Many different preparations of *opium* have been advised in this state of the gout. They are all hurtful if given before the morbid action of the system is nearly reduced. It should then be given in small doses accommodated to the excitability of the system.

Applications of various kinds to the affected limbs have been used in a fit of the gout, and some of them with success. The late Dr. Chalmers of South-Carolina used to meet the pain of the gout as soon as it fixed in any of his limbs, with a blister, and generally removed it by that means in two or three days. I have imitated this practice in several cases, and always with success, nor have I ever seen the gout thrown upon any of the viscera by means of this remedy. Caustics have sometimes been applied to gouty limbs with advantage. The moxa described and used by sir William Temple, which is nothing but culinary fire, has often not only given relief to a pained limb, but carried off a fit of the gout in a few hours. These powerful applications may be used with equal advantage in those cases in which the gout by falling upon the head produces coma, or symptoms of apoplexy. A large caustic to the neck roused Mr. John M. Nesbit from a coma in which he had lain for three days, and thereby appeared to save his life. Blisters, and cataplasms of mustard, had been previously used to different parts of his body, but without the least effect. In cases of moderate pain, where a blister has been objected to, I have seen a cabbage leaf afford considerable relief. It produces a moisture upon the part affected, without exciting any pain. An old sea captain taught me to apply molasses to a limb inflamed or pained by the gout. I have frequently advised it, and generally with advantage. All volatile and stimulating liniments are improper, for they not only endanger a translation of the morbid excitement to the viscera, but where they have not this effect, they increase the pain and inflammation of the part affected.

The sooner a patient exercises his lower limbs by walking, after a fit of the gout, the better. "I made it a constant rule (says Mr. Small) to walk abroad as soon as the inflammatory state of the gout was past, and though by so doing, I often suffered great pain, I am well convinced that the free use I now enjoy of my limbs is chiefly owing to my determined perseverance in the use of that exercise; nor am I less persuaded that nine in ten of gouty cripples owe their lameness more to indolence, and fear of pain, than to the genuine effects of the gout[65]." Sir William Temple confirms the propriety of Mr. Small's opinion and practice, by an account of an old man who obviated a fit of the gout as often as he felt it coming in his feet, by walking in the open air, and afterwards by going into a warm bed, and having the parts well rubbed where the pain began. "By following this course (he says) he was never laid up with the gout, and before his death recommended the same course to his son if ever he should fall into that accident." Under a conviction of the safety of this practice the same author concludes the history of his own case in the following words: "I favoured it [viz. the swelling in my feet] all this while more than I needed, upon the common opinion, that walking too much might draw down the humour, which I have since had reason to conclude is a great mistake, and that if I had walked as much as I could from the first day the pain left me, the swelling might have left me too in a much less time[66]."

III. I come now to mention the remedies which are proper in that state of the gout in which a *feeble* morbid action takes place in the blood-vessels and viscera.

I shall begin this head, by remarking, that this state of the gout is often created, like the typhus state of fever, by the neglect, or too scanty use of evacuations in its first stage. When the prejudices which now prevent the adoption of those remedies in their proper time, are removed, we shall hear but little of the low state of the arthritic fever, nor of the numerous diseases from obstruction which are produced by the blood-vessels disorganizing the viscera, by repeated and violent attacks of the disease.

To determine the character of a paroxysm of gout and the remedies proper to relieve it, the climate, the season of the year, the constitution of the atmosphere, and the nature of the prevailing epidemic, should be carefully attended to by a physician. But his principal dependence should be placed upon the state of the pulse. If it do not discover the marks which indicate bleeding formerly referred to, but is weak, quick, and soft, the remedies should be such as are calculated to produce a more vigorous, and equable action in the blood-vessels and viscera. They are,

1. *Opium.* It should at first be given in small doses, and afterwards increased, as circumstances may require.

2. *Madeira* or *Sherry wine* alone, or diluted with water, or in the form of whey, or rendered more cordial by having any agreeable spice infused in it. It may be given cold or warm, according to the taste of the patient, or the state of his stomach. If this medicine be rejected in all the above forms,

3. *Porter* should be given. It is often retained when no other liquor will lie upon the stomach. I think I once saved the life of Mr. Nesbit by this medicine. It checked a vomiting, from the gout, which seemed to be the last symptom of his departing life. If porter fail of giving relief,

4. *Ardent spirits* should be given, either alone, or in the form of grog, or toddy. Cases have occurred in which a pint of brandy has been taken in the course of an hour with advantage. Great benefit has sometimes been found from Dr. Warner's tincture, in this state of the gout. As these observations may fall into the hands of persons who may not have access to Dr. Warner's book, I shall here insert the receipt for preparing it.

Of raisins, sliced and stoned, half a pound.

Rhubarb, one ounce.

Sena, two drachms.

Coriander and fennel seeds, of each one drachm.

Cochineal, saffron, and liquorice root, each half a drachm.

Infuse them for ten days in a quart of French brandy, then strain it, and add a pint more of brandy to the ingredients, afterwards strain it, and mix both tinctures together. Four table spoons full of this cordial are to be taken every hour, mixed with an equal quantity of water, until relief be obtained.

Ten drops of laudanum may be added to each dose in those cases in which the cordial does not produce its intended effects, in two or three hours. If all the different forms of ardent spirits which have been mentioned fail of giving relief,

5. From 30 drops to a tea spoonful of *æther* should be given in any agreeable vehicle. Also,

6. *Volatile alkali.* From five to ten grains of this medicine should be given every two hours.

7. *Aromatic substances,* such as alspice, ginger, Virginia snake-root, cloves, and mace in the form of teas, have all been useful in this state of the gout.

All these remedies are indicated in a more especial manner when the gout affects the stomach. They are likewise proper when it affects the bowels. The laudanum in this case should be given by way of glyster. After the vomiting was checked in Mr. Nesbit by means of porter, he was afflicted with a dull and distressing pain in his bowels, which was finally removed by two anodyne glysters injected daily for two or three weeks.

8. Where the gout produces spasmodic or convulsive motions, the *oil of amber* may be given with advantage. I once saw it remove for a while a convulsive cough from the gout.

9. In cases where the stomach will bear the *bark*, it should be given in large and frequent doses. It does the same service in this state of gout, that it does in the slow, or low states of fever from any other cause. Where the gout appears in the form of an intermittent, the bark affords the same relief that it does in the same disease from autumnal exhalations. Mr. Small found great benefit from it after discharging the contents of his stomach and bowels by a dose of tartar emetic. "I do not call (says this gentleman) a fit of the gout a paroxysm, for there are several paroxysms in the fit, each of which is ushered in with a rigour, sickness at stomach, and subsequent heat. In this the gout bears a resemblance to an irregular intermittent, at least to a remitting fever, and hence perhaps the efficacy of the bark in removing the gout[67]."

10. The *warm bath* is a powerful remedy in exciting a regular and healthy action in the sanguiferous system. Where the patient is too weak to be taken

out of bed, and put into a bathing tub, his limbs and body should be wrapped in flannels dipped in warm water. In case of a failure of all the above remedies,

11. A *salivation* should be excited as speedily as possible, by means of mercury. Dr. Cheyne commends it in high terms. I have once used it with success. The mercury, when used in this way, brings into action an immense mass of latent excitement, and afterwards diffuses it equally through every part of the body.

12. Besides these internal remedies, frictions with brandy, and volatile liniment, should be used to the stomach and bowels. Blisters should be applied to parts in which congestion or pain is seated, and stimulating cataplasms should be applied to the lower limbs. The flour of mustard has been justly preferred for this purpose. It should be applied to the upper part of the foot.

The reader will perceive, in the account I have given of the remedies proper in the feeble state of chronic fever, that they are the same which are used in the common typhus, or what is called nervous fever. There is no reason why they should not be the same, for the supposed two morbid states of the system are but one disease.

It is agreeable in medical researches to be under the direction of principles. They render unnecessary, in many instances, the slow and expensive operations of experience, and thus multiply knowledge, by lessening labour. The science of navigation has rested upon this basis, since the discovery of the loadstone. A mariner who has navigated a ship to one distant port, is capable of conducting her to every port on the globe. In like manner, the physician who can cure one disease by a knowledge of its principles, may by the same means cure all the diseases of the human body, for their causes are the same. Judgment is required, only in accommodating the force of remedies to the force of each disease. The difference in diseases which arises from their seats, from age, sex, habit, season, and climate, may be known in a short time, and is within the compass of very moderate talents.

IV. Were I to enumerate all the local symptoms of gout which occur without fever, and the remedies that are proper to relieve them, I should be led into a tedious digression. The reader must consult practical books for an account of them. I shall only mention the remedies for a few of them.

The theory of the gout which has been delivered, will enable us to understand the reason why a disease which properly belongs to the whole system, should at any time be accompanied only with local morbid affection. The whole body is a unit, and hence morbid impressions which are resisted by sound parts are propagated to such as are weak, where they excite those morbid actions we call disease.

The *head-ach* is a distressing symptom of the gout. It yields to depleting or tonic remedies, according to the degree of morbid action which accompanies it. I have heard an instance of an old man, who was cured of an obstinate head-ach by throwing aside his nightcap, and sleeping with his bare head exposed to the night air. The disease in this case was probably attended with great morbid action. In this state of the vessels of the brain, cupping, cold applications to the head, purges, a temperate diet, and blisters behind the ears, are all proper remedies, and should be used together, or in succession, as the nature of the disease may require. Many persons have been cured of the same complaint by sleeping in woollen nightcaps. The morbid action in these cases is always of a feeble nature. With this remedy, tonics, particularly the bark and cold bath, will be proper. I have once known a chronic gouty pain in the head cured by an issue in the arm, after pounds of bark, and many other tonic remedies, had been taken to no purpose.

The *ophthalmia* from gout should be treated with the usual remedies for that disease when it arises from other causes, with the addition of such local applications to other and distant parts of the body, as may abstract the gouty action from the eyes.

Dull but constant pains in the limbs yield to frictions, volatile liniments, muslin and woollen worn next to the skin, electricity, a salivation, and the warm and cold bath. A gentleman who was afflicted with a pain of this kind for three years and a half in one of his arms, informed me, that he had been cured by wearing a woollen stocking that had been boiled with sulphur in water, for two weeks upon the affected limb. He had previously worn flannel upon it, but without receiving any benefit from it. I have known wool and cotton, finely carded, and made into small mats, worn upon the hips, when affected by gout, with great advantage. In obstinate sciatic pains, without fever or inflammation, Dr. Pitcairn's remedy, published by Dr. Cheyne, has performed many cures. It consists in taking from one to four tea-spoons full of the fine spirit of turpentine every morning, for a week or ten days, in three times the quantity of honey, and afterwards in drinking a large quantity of sack whey, to settle it on the stomach, and carry it into the blood. An anodyne should be taken every night after taking this medicine.

A *gouty diarrhœa* should be treated with the usual astringent medicines of the shops. Blisters to the wrists and ankles, also a salivation, have often cured it. I have heard of its being checked, after continuing for many years, by the patient eating large quantities of alspice, which he carried loose in his pocket for that purpose.

The *angina pectoris*, which I have said is a symptom of the gout, generally comes on with fulness and tension in the pulse. After these are reduced by two or three bleedings, mineral tonics seldom fail of giving relief.

Spasms in the stomach, and *pains in the bowels*, often seize gouty people in the midst of business or pleasure, or in the middle of the night. My constant prescription for these complaints is ten drops of laudanum every half hour, till relief be obtained. If this medicine be taken in the forming state of these pains, a single dose generally removes the disease. It is preferable to spiced wine and spirits, inasmuch as it acts quicker, and leaves no disposition to contract a love for it when it is not required to ease pain.

The *pain in the rectum* which has been described, yields to the common remedies for the piles. Cold water applied to the part, generally gives immediate relief.

For a *preternatural secretion and excretion of bile*, gentle laxatives, and abstinence from oily food, full meals, and all violent exercises of the body and mind, are proper.

The *itching in the anus*, which I have supposed to be a symptom of gout, has yielded in one instance that has come within my knowledge to mercurial ointment applied to the part affected. Dr. Lettsom recommends fomenting the part with a decoction of poppy heads and hemlock, and advises lenient purges and a vegetable diet as a radical cure for the disease[68].

For the *itching in the vagina* I have found a solution of the sugar of lead in water to be an excellent palliative application. Dr. Lettsom recommends as a cure for it, the use of bark in delicate habits, and occasional bleeding, with a light and moderate diet, if it occur about the time of the cessation of the menses.

Obstinate *cutaneous eruptions*, which are the effects of gout, have been cured by gentle physic, a suitable diet, issues, and applications of the unguentum citrinum to the parts affected.

The *arthritic gonorrhœa* should be treated with the same remedies as a gonorrhœa from any other cause.

In the treatment of all the local symptoms that have been enumerated, it will be of great consequence to inquire, before we attempt to cure them, whether they have not succeeded general gout, and thereby relieved the system from its effects in parts essential to life. If this have been the case, the cure of them should be undertaken with caution, and the danger of a local disease being exchanged for a general one, should be obviated by remedies that are calculated to eradicate the gouty diathesis altogether from the system. The means for this purpose, agreeably to our order, come next under our consideration. Before I enter upon this head, I shall premise, that I do not admit of the seeds of the gout remaining in the body to be eliminated by art after a complete termination of one of its paroxysms, any more than I admit of the seeds of a pleurisy or intermitting fever remaining in the body, after they have been cured by blood-letting or bark. A predisposition only remains in the system to a return of the gout, from its usual remote and exciting causes. The contrary idea took its rise in those ages of medicine in which morbific matter was supposed to be the proximate cause of the gout, but it has unfortunately continued since the rejection of that theory. Thus in many cases we see wrong habits continue long after the principles have been discarded, from which they were derived.

I have known several instances in which art, and I have heard and read of others in which accidental suffering from abstinence, pain, and terror have been the happy means of overcoming a predisposition to the gout. A gentleman from one of the West-India islands, who had been for many years afflicted with the gout, was perfectly cured of it by living a year or two upon the temperate diet of the jail in this city, into which he was thrown for debt by one of his creditors. A large hæmorrhage from the foot, inflamed and swelled by the gout, accidentally produced by a penknife which fell upon it, effected in an Irish gentleman a lasting cure of the disease. Hildanus mentions the history of a gentleman, whom he knew intimately, who was radically cured of a gout with which he had been long afflicted, by the extreme bodily pain he suffered innocently from torture in the canton of Berne. He lived to be an old man, and ever afterwards enjoyed good health[69]. The following letter from my brother contains the history of a case in which terror suddenly eradicated the gout from the system.

"Reading, July 27th, 1797.

"DEAR BROTHER,

"WHEN I had the pleasure of seeing you last week, I mentioned an extraordinary cure of the gout in this town, by means of a *fright.* In compliance with your request, I now send an exact narration of the facts.

"Peter Fether, the person cured, is now alive, a householder in Reading, seventy-three years of age, a native of Germany, and a very hearty man. The first fit of the gout he ever had, was about the year 1773; and from that time till 1785, he had a regular attack in the spring of every year. His feet, hands, and elbows were much swollen and inflamed; the fits lasted long, and were excruciating. In particular, the last fit in 1785 was so severe, as to induce an apprehension, that it would inevitably carry him off, when he was suddenly relieved by the following accident.

"As he lay in a small back room adjoining the yard, it happened that one of his sons, in turning a waggon and horses, drove the tongue of the waggon with such force against the window, near which the old man lay stretched on a bed, as to beat in the sash of the window, and to scatter the pieces of broken glass all about him. To such a degree was he alarmed by the noise and violence, that he instantly leaped out of bed, forgot that he had ever used crutches, and eagerly inquired what was the matter. His wife, hearing the uproar, ran into the room, where, to her astonishment, she found her husband on his feet, bawling against the author of the mischief, with the most passionate vehemence. From *that* moment, he has been entirely exempt from the gout, has never had the slightest touch of it, and *now* enjoys perfect health, has a good appetite, and says he was never heartier in his life. This is probably the more remarkable, when I add, that he has always been used to the hard work of a farm, and *since* the year 1785 has frequently mowed in his own meadow, which I understand is low and wet. I am well informed, in his mode of living, he has been temperate, occasionally indulging in a glass of wine, after the manner of the German farmers, but not to excess.

"To you, who have been long accustomed to explore diseases, I leave the task of developing the principles, on which this mysterious restoration from the lowest decrepitude and bodily wretchedness, to a state of perfect health, has been accomplished. I well know that tooth-achs, head-achs, hiccoughs, [**AMP]c. are often removed by the sudden impression of fear, and that they return again. But to see a debilitated gouty frame instantly restored to vigour; to see the whole system in a moment, as it were, undergo a perfect and entire change, and the most inveterate and incurable disease *radically* expelled, is surely a *different* thing, and must be acknowledged a very singular and marvellous event. If an old man, languishing under disease and infirmity, had *died* of mere fright, nobody would have been surprised at it; but that he should be absolutely cured, and his constitution renovated by it, is a most extraordinary fact, which, while I am compelled to believe by unexceptionable evidence, I am totally at a loss to account for.

I am your sincerely
affectionate brother,
JACOB RUSH."

These facts, and many similar ones which might be mentioned, afford ample encouragement to proceed in enumerating the means which are proper to prevent the recurrence of the gout, or, in other words, to eradicate it from the system.

V. I shall first mention the means of preventing the return of that state of the disease which is accompanied with *violent* action, and afterwards take notice of the means of preventing the return of that state of it, in which a *feeble* morbid action takes place in the blood-vessels. The means for this purpose consist in avoiding all the remote, exciting, and predisposing causes of the gout which have been mentioned. I shall say a few words upon the most important of them, in the order that has been proposed.

I. The first remedy for obviating the *violent* state of gout is,

1. *Temperance.* This should be regulated in its degrees by the age, habits, and constitution of the patient. A diet consisting wholly of milk, vegetables, and simple water, has been found necessary to prevent the recurrence of the gout in some cases. But, in general, fish, eggs, the white meats and weak broths may be taken in small quantities once a day, with milk and vegetables at other times. A little salted meat, which affords less nourishment than fresh, may be eaten occasionally. It imparts vigour to the stomach, and prevents dyspepsia from a diet consisting chiefly of vegetables. The low and acid wines should be avoided, but weak Madeira or sherry wine and water, or small beer, may be drunken at meals. The latter liquor was the favourite drink of Dr. Sydenham in his fits of the gout. Strong tea and coffee should not be tasted, where there is reason to believe the habitual use of them has contributed to bring on the disease.

From the disposition of the gout to return in the spring and autumn, greater degrees of abstinence in eating and drinking will be necessary at those seasons than at any other time. With this diminution of aliment, gentle purges should be taken, to obviate an attack of the gout. In persons above fifty years of age, an abstemious mode of living should be commenced with great caution. It has sometimes, when entered upon suddenly, and carried to its utmost extent, induced fits of the gout, and precipitated death. In such persons, the abstractions from their usual diet should be small, and our dependence should be placed upon other means to prevent a return of the disease.

2. *Moderate labour* and *gentle exercise* have frequently removed that debility and vibratility in the blood-vessels, on which a predisposition to the gout depends. Hundreds of persons who have been reduced by misfortunes to the necessity of working for their daily bread, have thrown off a gouty diathesis derived from their patents, or acquired by personal acts of folly and intemperance. The employments of agriculture afford the most wholesome labour, and walking, the most salutary exercise. To be useful, they should be moderate. The extremes of indolence and bodily activity meet in a point. They both induce debility, which predisposes to a recurrence of a fit of the

gout. Riding in a carriage, and on horseback, are less proper as a means of preventing the disease than walking. Their action upon the body is partial. The lower limbs derive no benefit from it, and on these the violent state of gout generally makes its first attack. In England, many domestic exercises have been contrived for gouty people, such as shuttle-cock, bullets, the chamber-horse, and the like, but they are all trifling in their effects, compared with labour, and exercise in the open air. The efficacy of the former of those prophylactic remedies will appear in a strong point of light, when we consider, how much the operation of the remote and exciting causes of the gout which act more or less upon persons in the humblest ranks of society, are constantly counteracted in their effects, by the daily labour which is necessary for their subsistence.

3. To prevent the recurrence of the gout, cold should be carefully avoided, more especially when it is combined with moisture. Flannel should be worn next to the skin in winter, and muslin in summer, in order to keep up a steady and uniform perspiration. Fleecy hosiery should be worn in cold weather upon the breast and knees, and the feet should be kept constantly warm and dry by means of socks and cork-soaled shoes. It was by wetting his feet, by standing two or three hours upon the damp ground, that colonel Miles produced the gout in his stomach and bowels which had nearly destroyed him in the year 1795.

4. Great moderation should be used by persons who are subject to the gout in the exercise of their understandings and passions. Intense study, fear, terror, anger, and even joy, have often excited the disease into action. It has been observed, that the political and military passions act with more force upon the system, than those which are of a social and domestic nature; hence generals and statesmen are so often afflicted with the gout, and that too, as was hinted in another place, in moments the most critical and important to the welfare of a nation. The combination of the exercises of the understanding, and the passion of avarice in gaming, have often produced an attack of this disease.

These facts show the necessity of gouty people subjecting their minds, with all their operations, to the government of reason and religion. The understanding should be exercised only upon light and pleasant subjects. No study should ever be pursued till it brings on fatigue; and, above all things, midnight, and even late studies should be strictly avoided. A gouty man should always be in bed at an early hour. This advice has the sanction of Dr. Sydenham's name, and experience proves its efficacy in all chronic diseases.

5. The venereal appetite should be indulged with moderation. And,

6. Costiveness should be prevented by all persons who wish to escape a return of violent fits of the gout. Sulphur is an excellent remedy for this

purpose. Dr. Cheyne commends it in high terms. His words are, "Sulphur is one of the best remedies in the intervals of the gout. In the whole extent of the materia medica, I know not a more safe and active medicine[70]." Two cases have come within my knowledge, in which it has kept off fits of the gout for several years, in persons who had been accustomed to have them once or twice a year. Rhubarb in small quantities chewed, or in the form of pills, may be taken to obviate costiveness, by persons who object to the habitual use of sulphur. Dr. Cheyne, who is lavish in his praises of that medicine as a gentle laxative, says, he "knew a noble lord of great worth and much gout, who, by taking from the hands of a quack a drachm of rhubarb, tinged with cochineal to disguise it, every morning for six weeks, lived in health, for four years after, without any symptom of it[71]."

I have said that abstinence should be enjoined with more strictness in the spring and autumn, than at any other time, to prevent a return of the gout. From the influence of the weather at those seasons in exciting febrile actions in the system, the loss of a pint of blood will be useful in some cases for the same purpose. It will be the more necessary if the gout has not paid its habitual visits to the system. The late Dr. Gregory had been accustomed to an attack of the gout every spring. Two seasons passed away without his feeling any symptoms of it. He began to flatter himself with a hope that the predisposition to the disease had left him. Soon afterwards he died suddenly of an apoplexy. The loss of a few ounces of blood at the usual time in which the gout affected him, would probably have protracted his life for many years. In the year 1796, in visiting a patient, I was accidentally introduced into a room where a gentleman from the Delaware state had been lying on his back for near six weeks with an acute fit of the gout. He gave me a history of his sufferings. His pulse was full and tense, and his whole body was covered with sweat from the intensity of his pain. He had not had his bowels opened for ten days. I advised purging and bleeding in his case. The very names of those remedies startled him, for he had adopted the opinion of the salutary nature of a fit of the gout, and therefore hugged his chains. After explaining the reason of my prescriptions, he informed me, in support of them, that he had escaped the gout but two years in twenty, and that in one of these two years he had been bled for a fall from his horse, and, in the other, his body had been reduced by a chronic fever, previously to the time of the annual visit of his gout.

As a proof of the efficacy of active, or passive depletion, in preventing the gout, it has been found that persons who sweat freely, either generally or partially, or who make a great deal of water, are rarely affected by it.

An epitome of all that has been said upon the means of preventing a return of the gout, may be delivered in a few words. A man who has had one fit of it, should consider himself in the same state as a man who has received the seeds of a malignant fever into his blood. He should treat his body as if it were a Florence flask. By this means he will probably prevent, during his life, the re-excitement of the disease.

Are *issues* proper to prevent the return of the violent state of gout? I have heard of an instance of an issue in the leg having been effectual for this purpose; but if the remedies before-mentioned be used in the manner that has been directed, so unpleasant a remedy can seldom be necessary.

Are *bitters* proper to prevent a return of this state of gout? It will be a sufficient answer to this question to mention, that the duke of Portland's powder, which is composed of bitter ingredients, excited a fatal gout in many people who used it for that purpose. I should as soon expect to see gold produced by the operations of fire upon copper or lead, as expect to see the gout prevented or cured by any medicine that acted upon the system, without the aid of more or less of the remedies that have been mentioned.

II. We come now, in the last place, to mention the remedies which are proper to prevent a return of that state of gout which is attended with a *feeble* morbid action in the blood-vessels and viscera.

This state of gout generally occurs in the evening of life, and in persons of delicate habits, or in such as have had their constitutions worn down by repeated attacks of the disease.

The remedies to prevent it are,

1. A *gently stimulating diet*, consisting of animal food well cooked, with sound old Madeira or sherry wine, or weak spirit and water. Salted, and even smoked meat may be taken, in this state of the system, with advantage. It is an agreeable tonic, and is less disposed to create plethora than fresh meat. Pickles and vinegar should seldom be tasted. They dispose to gouty spasms in the stomach and bowels. Long intervals between meals should be carefully avoided. The stomach, when overstretched or empty, is always alike predisposed to disease. There are cases in which the evils of inanition in the stomach will be prevented, by a gouty patient eating in the middle of the night.

2. The use of *chalybeate medicines*. These are more safe when used habitually, than bitters. I have long been in the practice of giving the different preparations of iron in large doses, in chronic diseases, and in that state of debility which disposes to them. A lady of a weak constitution informed Dr. Cheyne, that she once asked Dr. Sydenham how long she might safely take

steel. His answer was, that "she might take it for thirty years, and then begin again if she continued ill[72]."

Water impregnated with iron, either by nature or art, may be taken instead of the solid forms of the metal. It will be more useful if it be drunken in a place where patients will have the benefit of country air.

3. The habitual use of the *volatile tincture of gum guiacum*, and of other cordial and gently stimulating medicines. A clove of garlic taken once or twice a day, has been found useful in debilitated habits predisposed to the gout. It possesses a wonderful power in bringing latent excitement into action. It moreover acts agreeably upon the nervous system.

Mr. Small found great benefit from breakfasting upon a tea made of half a drachm of ginger cut into small slices, in preventing occasional attacks of the gout in his stomach. Sir Joseph Banks was much relieved by a diet of milk, with ginger boiled in it. The root of the sassafras of our country might probably be used with advantage for the same purpose. Aurelian speaks of certain remedies for the gout which he calls "annalia[73]." The above medicines belong to this class. To be effectual, they should be persisted in, not for one year only, but for many years.

4. *Warmth*, uniformly applied, by means of suitable dresses, and sitting rooms, to every part of the body.

5. The *warm bath* in winter, and the *temperate*, or *cold bath* in summer.

6. *Exercise.* This may be in a carriage, or on horseback. The viscera being debilitated in this state of predisposition to the gout, are strengthened in a peculiar manner by the gentle motion of a horse. Where this or other modes of passive exercise cannot be had, frictions to the limbs and body should be used every day.

7. *Costiveness* should be avoided by taking occasionally one or two table spoons full of Dr. Warner's purging tincture prepared by infusing rhubarb, orange peel, and caraway seeds, of each an ounce, for three days in a quart of Madeira, or any other white wine. If this medicine be ineffectual for opening the bowels, rhubarb may be taken in the manner formerly mentioned.

8. The understanding and passions should be constantly employed in agreeable studies and pursuits. Fatigue of mind and body should be carefully avoided.

9. A warm climate often protracts life in persons subject to this state of gout. The citizens of Rome who had worn down their constitutions by

intemperance, added many years to their lives, by migrating to Naples, and enjoying there, in a warmer sun, the pure air of the Mediterranean, and sir William Temple says the Portuguese obtain the same benefit by transporting themselves to the Brazils, after medicine and diet cease to impart vigour to their constitutions in their native country.

Thus have I enumerated the principal remedies for curing and preventing the gout. Most of them are to be met with in books of medicine, but they have been administered by physicians, or taken by patients with so little regard to the different states of the system, that they have in many instances done more harm than good. Solomon places all wisdom, in the management of human affairs, in finding out the proper times for performing certain actions. Skill in medicine, consists in an eminent degree in timing remedies. There is a time to bleed, and a time to withhold the lancet. There is a time to give physic, and a time to trust to the operations of nature. There is a time to eat meat, and there is a time to abstain from it. There is a time to give tonic medicines, and a time to refrain from them. In a word, the cure of the gout depends wholly upon two things, viz. *proper* remedies, in their proper *times*, and *places*.

I shall take leave of this disease, by comparing it to a deep and dreary cave in a new country, in which ferocious beasts and venomous reptiles, with numerous ghosts and hobgoblins, are said to reside. The neighbours point at the entrance of this cave with horror, and tell of the many ravages that have been committed upon their domestic animals, by the cruel tenants which inhabit it. At length a school-boy, careless of his safety, ventures to enter this subterraneous cavern, when! to his great delight, he finds nothing in it but the same kind of stones and water he left behind him upon the surface of the earth. In like manner, I have found no other principles necessary to explain the cause of the gout, and no other remedies necessary to cure it, than such as are admitted in explaining the causes, and in prescribing for the most simple and common diseases.

Footnotes:

[58] Volume IV.

[59] Medical Memoirs, vol. III.

[60] Medical Reports on the Effects of Hot and Cold Water, p. 215.

[61] Defence of Blood-letting, vol. IV.

[62] Medical Observations and Inquiries, vol VI. p. 201.

[63] Physical and Literary Essays, vol. III. p. 469.

[64] Defence of Blood-letting.

[65] Medical Observations and Inquiries, vol. vi. p. 220.

[66] Essay upon the Cure of the Gout by Moxa, vol. i. folio edition, p. 143 and 141.

[67] Medical Observations and Inquiries, vol. vi. p. 220.

[68] Medical Memoirs, vol. III.

[69] Observat. Chirurg. Cent. 1. Obs. 79.

[70] Essay on the Nature and True Method of Treating the Gout, p. 36.

[71] Page 30.

[72] Essay on the Nature, and True Method of Treating the Gout, p. 69.

[73] Morborum Chronicorum. Lib. v. Cap. 2.

OBSERVATIONS
UPON
THE NATURE AND CURE
OF THE
HYDROPHOBIA.

In entering upon the consideration of this formidable disease, I feel myself under an involuntary impression, somewhat like that which was produced by the order the king of Syria gave to his captains when he was conducting them to battle: "Fight not with small or great, save only with the king of Israel[74]." In whatever light we contemplate the hydrophobia, it may be considered as pre-eminent in power and mortality, over all other diseases.

It is now many years since the distress and horror excited by it, both in patients and their friends, led me with great solicitude to investigate its nature. I have at length satisfied myself with a theory of it, which, I hope, will lead to a rational and successful mode of treating it.

For a history of the symptoms of the disease, and many interesting facts connected with it, I beg leave to refer the reader to Dr. Mease's learned and ingenious inaugural dissertation, published in the year 1792.

The remote and exciting causes of the hydrophobia are as follow:

1. The bite of a rabid animal. Wolves, foxes, cats, as well as dogs, impart the disease. It has been said that blood must be drawn in order to produce it, but I have heard of a case in Lancaster county, in Pennsylvania, in which a severe contusion, by the teeth of the rabid animal, without the effusion of a drop of red blood, excited the disease. Happily for mankind, it cannot be communicated by blood, or saliva falling upon sound parts of the body. In Maryland, the negroes eat with safety the flesh of hogs that have perished from the bite of mad dogs; and I have heard of the milk of a cow, at Chestertown, in the same state, having been used without any inconvenience by a whole family, on the very day in which she was affected by this disease, and which killed her in a few hours. Dr. Baumgarten confirms these facts by saying, that "the flesh and milk of rabid animals have been eaten with perfect impunity[75]."

In the following observations I shall confine myself chiefly to the treatment of the hydrophobia which arises from the bite of a rabid animal, but I shall add in this place a short account of all its other causes.

2. Cold night air. Dr. Arthaud, late president of the society of Philadelphians in St. Domingo, has published several cases in which it was produced in negroes by sleeping all night in the open air.

3. A wound in a tendinous part.

4. Putrid and impure animal food.

5. Worms.

6. Eating beech nuts.

7. Great thirst.

8. Exposure to intense heat.

9. Drinking cold water when the body was very much heated.

10. A fall.

11. Fear.

12. Hysteria.

13. Epilepsy.

14. Tetanus.

15. Hydrocephalus. Of the presence of hydrophobia in the hydrocephalic state of fever, there have been several instances in Philadelphia.

16. An inflammation of the stomach.

17. The dysentery.

18. The typhus fever. Dr. Trotter mentions the hydrophobia as a symptom which frequently occurred in the typhus state of fever in the British navy[76].

19. It is taken notice of likewise in a putrid fever by Dr. Coste[77]; and Dr. Griffitts observed it in a high degree in a young lady who died of the yellow fever, in 1793.

20. The bite of an angry, but not a diseased animal.

21. An involuntary association of ideas.

Cases of spontaneous hydrophobia from all the above causes are to be met with in practical writers, and of most of them in M. Audry's learned work, entitled, "Recherches sur la Rage."

The dread of water, from which this disease derives its name, has five distinct grades. 1. It cannot be drunken. 2. It cannot be touched. 3. The sound of it pouring from one vessel to another, 4. the sight of it, and 5. even the naming of it, cannot be borne, without exciting convulsions. But this symptom is not a universal one. Dr. Mead mentions three cases in which there was no dread of water, in persons who received the disease from the bite of a rabid animal. It is unfortunate for this disease, as well as many others, that a single symptom should impose names upon them. In the present instance it has done great harm, by fixing the attention of physicians so exclusively upon the dread of water which occurs in it, that they have in a great measure overlooked every other circumstance which belongs to the disease. The theory of the hydrophobia, which an examination of its causes, symptoms, and accidental cures, with all the industry I was capable of, has led me to adopt, is, that it is a *malignant state of fever*. My reasons for this opinion are as follow:

1. The disease in all rabid animals is a fever. This is obvious in dogs who are most subject to it. It is induced in them by the usual causes of fever, such as scanty or putrid aliment[78], extreme cold, and the sudden action of heat upon their bodies. Proofs of its being derived from each of the above causes are to be met with in most of the authors who have written upon it. The animal matters which are rendered morbid by the action of the above causes upon them, are determined to the saliva, in which a change seems to be induced, similar to that which takes place in the perspirable matter of the human species from the operation of similar causes upon it. This matter, it is well known, is the remote cause of the jail fever. No wonder the saliva of a dog should produce a disease of the same kind, after being vitiated by the same causes, and thereby disposed to produce the same effects.

2. The disease called canine madness, prevails occasionally among dogs at those times in which malignant fevers are epidemic. This will not surprise those persons who have been accustomed to observe the prevalence of the influenza and bilious fevers among other domestic animals at a time when they are epidemic among the human species.

3. Dogs, when they are said to be mad, exhibit the usual symptoms of fever, such as a want of appetite, great heat, a dull, fierce, red, or watery eye, indisposition to motion, sleepiness, delirium, and madness. The symptom of madness is far from being universal, and hence many dogs are diseased and die with this malignant fever, that are inoffensive, and instead of biting, continue to fawn upon their masters. Nor is the disposition of the fever to communicate itself by infection universal among dogs any more than the same fever in the human species, and this I suppose to be one reason why many people are bitten by what are called mad dogs, who never suffer any inconvenience from it.

4. A dissection of a dog, by Dr. Cooper, that died with this fever, exhibited all the usual marks of inflammation and effusion which take place in common malignant fevers. I shall in another place mention a fifth argument in favour of the disease in dogs being a malignant fever, from the efficacy of one of the most powerful remedies in that state of fever, having cured it in two instances.

II. The disease produced in the human species by the bite of a rabid animal, is a *malignant* fever. This appears first from its symptoms. These, as recorded by Aurelian, Mead, Fothergill, Plummer, Arnold, Baumgarten, and Morgagni, are chills, great heat, thirst, nausea, a burning sensation in the stomach, vomiting, costiveness; a small, quick, tense, irregular, intermitting, natural, or slow pulse; a cool skin, great sensibility to cold air, partial cold and clammy sweats on the hands, or sweats accompanied with a warm skin diffused all over the body, difficulty of breathing, sighing, restlessness, hiccup, giddiness, head-ach, delirium, coma, false vision, dilatation of the pupils, dulness of sight, blindness, glandular swellings, heat of urine, priapism, palpitation of the heart, and convulsions. I know that there are cases of hydrophobia upon record, in which there is said to be a total absence of fever. The same thing has been said of the plague. In both cases the supposed absence of fever is the effect of stimulus acting upon the blood-vessels with so much force as to suspend morbid action in them. By abstracting a part of this stimulus, a fever is excited, which soon discovers itself in the pulse and on the skin, and frequently in pains in every part of the body. The dread of water, and the great sensibility of the system to cold air, are said to give a specific character to the hydrophobia; but the former symptom, it has been often seen, occurs in diseases from other causes, and the latter has been frequently observed in the yellow fever. It is no more extraordinary that a fever excited by the bite of a rabid animal should excite a dread of water, than that fevers from other causes should produce aversion from certain aliments, from light, and from sounds of all kinds; nor is it any more a departure from the known laws of stimulants, that the saliva of a mad dog should affect the fauces, than that mercury should affect the salivary glands. Both stimuli appear to act in a specific manner.

2. The hydrophobia partakes of the character of a malignant fever, in appearing at different intervals from the time in which the infection is received into the body. These intervals are from one day to five or six months. The small-pox shows itself in intervals from eight to twenty days, and the plague and yellow fever from the moment in which the miasmata are inhaled, to nearly the same distance of time. This latitude in the periods at which infectious and contagious matters are brought into action in the body,

must be resolved into the influence which the season of the year, the habits of the patients, and the passion of fear have upon them.

Where the interval between the time of being bitten, and the appearance of a dread of water, exceeds five or six months, it is probable it may be occasioned by a disease derived from another cause. Such a person is predisposed in common with other people to all the diseases of which the hydrophobia is a symptom. The recollection of the poisonous wound he has received, and its usual consequences, is seldom absent from his mind for months or years. A fever, or an affection of his nerves from their most common causes, cannot fail of exciting in him apprehensions of the disease which usually follows the accident to which he has been exposed. His fears are then let loose upon his system, and produce in a short time a dread of water which appears to be wholly unconnected with the bite of a rabid animal. Similar instances of the effects of fear upon the human body are to be met with in books of medicine. The pains produced by fear acting upon the imagination in supposed venereal infections, are as real and severe as they are in the worst state of that disease.

3. Blood drawn in the hydrophobia exhibits the same appearances which have been remarked in malignant fevers. In Mr. Bellamy, the gentleman whose case is so minutely related by Dr. Fothergill, the blood discovered with "slight traces of size, *serum* remarkably *yellow.*" It was uncommonly sizy in a boy of Mr. George Oakley whom I saw, and bled for the first time, on the fourth day of his disease, in the beginning of the year 1797. His pulse imparted to the fingers the same kind of quick and tense stroke which is common in an acute inflammatory fever. He died in convulsions the next day. He had been bitten by a mad dog on one of his temples, three weeks before he discovered any signs of indisposition. There are several other cases upon record, of the blood exhibiting, in this disease, the same appearances as in common malignant and inflammatory fevers.

4. The hydrophobia accords exactly with malignant fevers in its duration. It generally terminates in death, according to its violence, and the habit of the patient, in the first, second, third, fourth, or fifth day, from the time of its attack, and with the same symptoms which attend the last stage of malignant fevers.

5. The body, after death from the hydrophobia, putrifies with the same rapidity that it does after death from a malignant fever in which no depletion has been used.

6. Dissections of bodies which have died of the hydrophobia, exhibit the same appearances which are observed in the bodies of persons who have perished of malignant fevers. These appearances, according to Morgagni and Tauvry[79], are marks of inflammation in the throat, œsophagus, trachea,

brain, stomach, liver, and bowels. Effusions of water, and congestions of blood in the brain, large quantities of dark-coloured or black bile in the gall-bladder and stomach, mortifications in the bowels and bladder, livid spots on the surface of the body, and, above all, the arteries filled with fluid blood, and the veins nearly empty. I am aware, that two cases of death from hydrophobia are related by Dr. Vaughan, in which no appearance of disease was discovered by dissection in any part of the body. Similar appearances have occasionally been met with in persons who have died of malignant fevers. In another place I hope to prove, that we err in placing disease in inflammation, for it is one of its primary effects only, and hence, as was before remarked, it does not take place in many instances in malignant fevers, until the arteries are so far relaxed by two or three bleedings, as to be able to relieve themselves by effusing red blood into serous vessels, and thus to produce that error loci which I shall say hereafter is essential to inflammation[80]. The existence of this grade of action in the arteries may always be known by the presence of sizy blood, and by the more obvious and common symptoms of fever.

The remedies for hydrophobia, according to the principles I have endeavoured to establish, divide themselves naturally into two kinds.

I. Such as are proper to prevent the disease, after the infection of the rabid animal is received into the body.

II. Such as are proper to cure it when formed.

The first remedy under the first general head is, abstracting or destroying the virus, by cutting or burning out the wounded part, or by long and frequent effusions of water upon it, agreeably to the advice of Dr. Haygarth, in order to wash the saliva from it. The small-pox has been prevented, by cutting out the part in which the puncture was made in the arm with variolous matter. There is no reason why the same practice should not succeed, if used in time, in the hydrophobia. Where it has failed of success, it has probably been used after the poison has contaminated the blood. The wound should be kept open and running for several months. In this way a servant girl, who was bitten by the same cat that bit Mr. Bellamy, is supposed by Dr. Fothergill to have escaped the disease. Dr. Weston of Jamaica believes that he prevented the disease by the same means, in two instances. Perhaps an advantage would arise from exciting a good deal of inflammation in the wound. We observe after inoculation, that the more inflamed the puncture becomes, and the greater the discharge from it, the less fever and eruption follow in the small-pox.

A second preventive is a low diet, such as has been often used with success to mitigate the plague and yellow fever. The system, in this case, bends beneath the stimulus of the morbid saliva, and thus obviates or lessens its effects at a future day.

During the use of these means to prevent the disease, the utmost care should be taken to keep up our patient's spirits, by inspiring confidence in the remedies prescribed for him.

Mercury has been used in order to prevent the disease. There are many well-attested cases upon record, of persons who have been salivated after being bitten by mad animals, in whom the disease did not show itself, but there are an equal number of cases to be met with, in which a salivation did not prevent it. From this it would seem probable, that the saliva did not infect in the cases in which the disease was supposed to have been prevented by the mercury. At the time calomel was used to prepare the body for the small-pox, a salivation was often induced by it. The affection of the salivary glands in many instances lessened the number of pock, but I believe in no instance prevented the eruptive fever.

I shall say nothing here of the many other medicines which have been used to prevent the disease. No one of them has, I believe, done any more good, than the boasted specifics which have been used to eradicate the gout, or to procure old age. They appear to have derived their credit from some of the following circumstances accompanying the bite of the animal.

1. The animal may have been angry, but not diseased with a malignant fever such as I have described.

2. He may have been diseased, but not to such a degree as to have rendered his saliva infectious.

3. The saliva, when infectious, may have been so washed off in passing through the patient's clothes, as not to have entered the wound made in the flesh. And

4. There may have been no predisposition in the patient to receive the fever. This is often observed in persons exposed to the plague, yellow fever, small-pox, and to the infection of the itch, and the venereal disease.

The hydrophobia, like the small-pox, generally comes on with some pain, and inflammation in the part in which the infection was infused into the body, but to this remark, as in the small-pox, there are some exceptions. As soon as the disease discovers itself, whether by pain or inflammation in the wounded part, or by any of the symptoms formerly mentioned, the first remedy indicated is *blood-letting*. All the facts which have been mentioned, relative to its cause, symptoms, and the appearances of the body after death, concur to enforce the use of the lancet in this disease. Its affinity to the plague and yellow fever in its force, is an additional argument in favour of that remedy. To be effectual, it should be used in the most liberal manner. The loss of 100 to 200 ounces of blood will probably be necessary in most cases to effect a cure. The pulse should govern the use of the lancet as in other states of fever, taking care not to be imposed upon by the absence of *frequency* in it, in the supposed absence of fever, and of *tension* in affections of the stomach, bowels, and brain. This practice, in the extent I have recommended it, is justified not only by the theory of the disease, but by its having been used with success in the following cases.

Dr. Nugent cured a woman by two copious bleedings, and afterwards by the use of sweating and cordial medicines.

Mr. Wrightson was encouraged by Dr. Nugent's success to use the same remedies with the same happy issue in a boy of 15 years of age[81].

Mr. Falconer cured a young woman of the name of Hannah Moore, by "a copious bleeding," and another depleting remedy to be mentioned hereafter[82]

Mr. Poupart cured a woman by bleeding until she fainted, and Mr. Berger gives an account of a number of persons being bitten by a rabid animal, all of whom died, except two who were saved by bleeding[83].

In the 40th volume of the Transactions of the Royal Society of London, there is an account of a man being cured of hydrophobia by Dr. Hartley, by the loss of 120 ounces of blood.

Dr. Tilton cured this disease in a woman in the Delaware state by very copious bleeding. The remedy was suggested to the doctor by an account taken from a London magazine of a dreadful hydrophobia being cured by an accidental and profuse hæmorrhage from the temporal artery[84].

A case is related by Dr. Innes[85], of the loss of 116 ounces of blood in seven days having cured this disease. In the patient who was the subject of this cure, the bleeding was used in the most depressed, and apparently weak state of the pulse. It rose constantly with the loss of blood.

The cases related by Dr. Tilton and Dr. Innes were said to be of a spontaneous nature, but the morbid actions were exactly the same in both patients with those which are derived from the bite of a rabid animal. There is but one remote cause of disease, and that is stimulus, and it is of no consequence in the disease now under consideration, whether the dread of water be the effect of the saliva of a rabid animal acting upon the fauces, or of a morbid excitement determined to those parts by any other stimulus. The inflammation of the stomach depends upon the same kind of morbid action, whether it be produced by the miasmata of the yellow fever, or the usual remote and exciting causes of the gout. An apoplexy is the same disease when it arises from a contusion by external violence, that it is when it arises spontaneously from the congestion of blood or water in the brain. A dropsy from obstructions in the liver induced by strong drink, does not differ in its proximate cause from the dropsy brought on by the obstructions in the same viscus which are left by a neglected, or half cured bilious fever. These remarks are of extensive application, and, if duly attended to, would deliver us from a mass of error which has been accumulating for ages in medicine: I mean the nomenclature of diseases from their remote causes. It is the most offensive and injurious part of the rubbish of our science.

I grant that bleeding has been used in some instances in hydrophobia without effect, but in all such cases it was probably used out of time, or in too sparing a manner. The credit of this remedy has suffered in many other diseases from the same causes. I beg it may not be tried in this disease, by any physician who has not renounced our modern systems of nosology, and adopted, in their utmost extent, the principles and practice of Botallus and Sydenham in the treatment of malignant fevers.

Before I quit the subject of blood-letting in hydrophobia, I have to add, that it has been used with success in two instances in dogs that had exhibited all the usual symptoms of what has been called madness. In one case, blood was drawn by cutting off the tail, in the other, by cutting off the ears of the diseased animal. I mention these facts with pleasure, not only because they serve to support the theory and practice which I have endeavoured to establish in this disease, but because they will render it unnecessary to destroy the life of a useful and affectionate animal in order to prevent his spreading it. By curing it in a dog by means of bleeding, we moreover beget confidence in the same remedy in persons who have been bitten by him, and thus lessen the force of the disease, by preventing the operation of fear upon the system.

2. Purges and glysters have been found useful in the hydrophobia. They discharge bile which is frequently vitiated, and reduce morbid action in the stomach and blood-vessels. Dr. Coste ascribes the cure of a young woman in a convent wholly to glysters given five or six times every day.

3. Sweating after bleeding completed the cure of the boy whose case is mentioned by Mr. Wrightson. Dr. Baumgarten speaks highly of this mode of depleting, and says further, that it has never been cured "but by evacuations of some kind."

4. All the advantages which attend a salivation in common malignant fevers, are to be expected from it in the hydrophobia. It aided blood-letting in two persons who were cured by Mr. Falconer and Dr. Le Compt.

There are several cases upon record in which musk and opium have afforded evident relief in this disease.

A physician in Virginia cured it by large doses of bark and wine. I have no doubt of the efficacy of these remedies when the disease is attended with a moderate or feeble morbid action in the system, for I take it for granted, it resembles malignant fevers from other causes in appearing in different grades of force. In its more violent and common form, stimulants of all kinds must do harm, unless they are of such a nature, and exhibited in such quantities, as to exceed in their force the stimulus of the disease; but this is not to be expected, more especially as the stomach is for the most part so irritable as sometimes to reject the mildest aliments as well as the most gentle medicines.

After the morbid actions in the system have been weakened, tonic remedies would probably be useful in accelerating the cure.

Blisters and stimulating cataplasms, applied to the feet, might probably be used with the same advantage in the declining state of the disease, that they have been used in the same stage of other malignant fevers.

The cold bath, also long immersion in cold water, have been frequently used in this disease. The former aided the lancet, in the cure of the man whose case is related by Dr. Hartley. There can be no objection to the cold water in either of the above forms, provided no dread is excited by it in the mind of the patient.

The reader will perceive here that I have deserted an opinion which I formerly held upon the cause and cure of the tetanus. I supposed the hydrophobia to depend upon debility. This debility I have since been led to consider as partial, depending upon abstraction of excitement from some, and a morbid accumulation of it in other parts of the body. The preternatural excitement predominates so far, in most cases of hydrophobia, over debility, that depleting remedies promise more speedily and safely to equalize, and render it natural, than medicines of an opposite character.

In the treatment of those cases of hydrophobia which are not derived from the bite of a rabid animal, regard should always be had to its remote and exciting causes, so as to accommodate the remedies to them.

The imperfection of the present nomenclature of medicine has become the subject of general complaint. The mortality of the disease from the bite of a rabid animal, has been increased by its name. The terms hydrophobia and canine madness, convey ideas of the symptoms of the disease only, and of such of them too as are by no means universal. If the theory I have delivered, and the practice I have recommended, be just, it ought to be called the hydrophobic state of fever. This name associates it at once with all the other states of fever, and leads us to treat it with the remedies which are proper in its kindred diseases, and to vary them constantly with the varying state of the system.

In reviewing what has been said of this disease, I dare not say that I have not been misled by the principles of fever which I have adopted; but if I have, I hope the reader will not be discouraged by my errors from using his reason in medicine. By contemplating those errors, he may perhaps avoid the shoals upon which I have been wrecked. In all his researches, let him ever remember that there is the same difference between the knowledge of a physician who prescribes for diseases as limited by genera and species, and of one who prescribes under the direction of just principles, that there is between the knowledge we obtain of the nature and extent of the sky, by viewing a few feet of it from the bottom of a well, and viewing from the top of a mountain the whole canopy of heaven.

Since the first edition of the foregoing observations, I have seen a communication to the editors of the Medical Repository[86], by Dr. Physick, which has thrown new light upon this obscure disease, and which, I hope, will aid the remedies that have been proposed, in rendering them more effectual for its cure. The doctor supposes death from hydrophobia to be the effect of a sudden and spasmodic constriction of the glottis, inducing suffocation, and that it might be prevented by creating an artificial passage for air into the lungs, whereby life might be continued long enough to admit of the disease being cured by other remedies. The following account of a dissection is intended to show the probability of the doctor's proposal being attended with success.

On the 13th of September, 1802, I was called, with Dr. Physick, to visit, in consultation with Dr. Griffitts, the son of William Todd, Esq. aged five years, who was ill with the disease called hydrophobia, brought on by the bite of a mad dog, on the 6th of the preceding month. The wound was small, and on his cheek, near his mouth, two circumstances which are said at all times to increase the danger of wounds from rabid animals. From the time he was bitten, he used the cold bath daily, and took the infusion, powder, and seeds of the anagallis, in succession, until the 9th of September, when he was seized with a fever which at first resembled the remittent of the season. Bleeding, purging, blisters, and the warm bath were prescribed for him, but without success. The last named remedy appeared to afford him some relief, which he manifested by paddling and playing in the water. At the time I saw him he was much agitated, had frequent twitchings, laughed often; but, with this uncommon excitement in his muscles and nerves, his mind was unusually correct in all its operations.

He discovered no dread of water, except in one instance, when he turned from it with horror. He swallowed occasionally about a spoon full of it at a time, holding the cup in his own hand, as if to prevent too great a quantity being poured at once into his throat. The quick manner of his swallowing, and the intervals between each time of doing so, were such as we sometimes observe in persons in the act of dying of acute diseases. Immediately after swallowing water, he looked pale, and panted for breath. He spoke rapidly, and with much difficulty. This was more remarkably the case when he attempted to pronounce the words *carriage*, *water*, and *river*. After speaking he panted for breath in the same manner that he did after drinking. He coughed and breathed as patients do in the moderate grade of the cynanche trachealis. The dog that had bitten him, Mr. Todd informed me, made a similar noise in attempting to bark, a day or two before he was killed. We proposed making an opening into his windpipe. To this his parents readily consented; but while we were preparing for the operation, such a change for the worse took place, that we concluded not to perform it. A cold sweat, with a feeble and quick pulse, came on; and he died suddenly, at 12 o'clock at night, about six hours after I first saw him. He retained his reason, and a playful humour, till the last minute of his life. An instance of the latter appeared in his throwing his handkerchief at his father just before he expired. The parents consented to our united request to examine his body. Dr. Griffitts being obliged to go into the country, and Dr. Physick being indisposed, I undertook this business the next morning; and, in the presence of Dr. John Dorsey (to whom I gave the dissecting knife), and my pupil Mr. Murduck, I discovered the following appearances. All the muscles of the neck had a livid colour, such as we sometimes observe, after death, in persons who have died of the sore throat. The muscles employed in deglutition and speech were suffused with blood. The epiglottis was inflamed, and the glottis so thickened and contracted, as barely to admit a probe of the common size. The trachea below it was likewise inflamed and thickened, and contained a quantity of mucus in it, such as we observe, now and then, after death from cynanche trachealis. The œsophagus exhibited no marks of disease; but the stomach had several inflamed spots upon it, and contained a matter of a brown appearance, and which emitted an offensive odour.

From the history of this dissection, and of many others, in which much fewer marks appeared of violent disease, in parts whose actions are essential to life, it is highly probable death is not induced in the ordinary manner in which malignant fevers produce it, but by a sudden or gradual suffocation. It is the temporary closure of this aperture which produces the dread of swallowing liquids: hence the reason why they are swallowed suddenly, and with intervals, in the manner that has been described; for, should the glottis be closed during the time of two swallows, in the highly diseased state of the system which takes place in this disease, suffocation would be the immediate and certain consequence. The same difficulty and danger attend the swallowing saliva, and hence the symptom of spitting, which has been so often taken notice of in hydrophobia. Solids are swallowed more easily than fluids, only because they descend by intervals, and because a less closure of the glottis is sufficient to favour their passage into the stomach. This remark is confirmed by the frequent occurrence of death in the very act of swallowing, and that too with the common symptoms of suffocation. To account for death from this cause, and in the manner that has been described, it will be necessary to recollect, that fresh air is more necessary to the action of the lungs in a fever than in health, and much more so in a fever of a malignant character, such as the hydrophobia appears to be, than in fevers of a milder nature. An aversion from swallowing liquids is not peculiar to this disease. It occurs occasionally in the yellow fever. It occurs likewise in the disease which has prevailed among the cats, both in Europe and America, and probably, in both instances, from a dread of suffocation in consequence of the closure of the glottis, and sudden abstraction of fresh air.

The seat of the disease, and the cause of death, being, I hope, thus ascertained, the means of preventing death come next under our consideration. Tonic remedies, in all their forms, have been administered to no purpose. The theory of the disease would lead us to expect a remedy for it in blood-letting. But this, though now and then used with success, is not its cure, owing, as we now see, to the mortal seat of the disease being so far removed from the circulation, as not to be affected by the loss of blood in the most liberal quantity. As well might we expect the inflammation and pain of a paronychia, or what is called a felon on the finger, to be removed by the same remedy. Purging and sweating, though occasionally successful, have failed in many instances; and even a salivation, when excited (which is rarely the case), has not cured it. An artificial aperture into the windpipe alone bids fair to arrest its tendency to death, by removing the symptom which generally induces it, and thereby giving time for other remedies, which have hitherto been unsuccessful, to produce their usual salutary effects in similar diseases[87]. In removing faintness, in drawing off the water in ischuria, in composing convulsions, and in stopping hæmorrhages in malignant fever, we do not cure the disease, but we prevent death, and thereby gain time for the use of the remedies which are proper to cure it. Laryngotomy, according to Fourcroy's advice, in diseases of the throat which obstruct respiration, should be preferred to tracheotomy, and the incision should be made in the triangular space between the thyroid and cricoid cartilages. Should this operation be adopted, in order to save life, it will not offer near so much violence to humanity as many other operations. We cut through a large mass of flesh into the bladder in extracting a stone. We cut into the cavity of the thorax in the operation for the empyema. We perforate the bones of the head in trepanning; and we cut through the uterus, in performing the Cæsarian operation, in order to save life. The operation of laryngotomy is much less painful and dangerous than any of them; and besides permitting the patient to breathe and to swallow, it is calculated to serve the inferior purpose of lessening the disease of the glottis by means of local depletion. After an aperture has been thus made through the larynx, the remedies should be such as are indicated by the state of the system, particularly by the state of the pulse. In hot climates it is, I believe, generally a disease of feeble re-action, and requires tonic remedies; but in the middle and northern states of America it is more commonly attended with so much activity and excitement of the blood-vessels, as to require copious blood-letting and other depleting remedies.

Should this new mode of attacking this furious disease be adopted, and become generally successful, the discovery will place the ingenious gentleman who suggested it in the first rank of the medical benefactors of mankind.

I have only to add a fact upon this subject which may tend to increase confidence in a mode of preventing the disease which has been recommended by Dr. Haygarth, and used with success in several instances. The same dog which bit Mr. Todd's son, bit, at the same time, a cow, a pig, a dog, and a black servant of Mr. Todd's. The cow and pig died; the dog became mad, and was killed by his master. The black man, who was bitten on one of his fingers, exposed the wound for some time, immediately after he received it, to a stream of pump water, and washed it likewise with soap and water. He happily escaped the disease, and is now in good health. That his wound was poisoned is highly probable, from its having been made eight hours after the last of the above animals was bitten, in which time there can be but little doubt of such a fresh secretion of saliva having taken place as would have produced the hydrophobia, had it not been prevented by the above simple remedy. I am not, however, so much encouraged by its happy issue in this case as to advise it in preference to cutting out the wounded part. It should only be resorted to where the fears of a patient, or his distance from a surgeon render it impossible to use the knife.

Footnotes:

[74] II. Chron. xviii. 30.

[75] Medical Commentaries, Philadelphia edition, vol. 7. p. 409.

[76] Medicina Nautica, p. 301.

[77] Medical Commentaries, Dobson's edition, vol. II. p. 476.

[78] "Animal food, in a state of putridity, is amongst the most frequent causes of canine madness."

"Canine madness chiefly arises from the excessive number of ill-kept and ill-fed dogs."

YOUNG'S ANNUALS, vol. XVII. p. 561.

[79] Bibliotheque Choisie de Medecine, tome XV. p. 210.

[80] In the 6th volume of the Medical Observations and Inquiries, there is an account of a dissection of a person who had been destroyed by taking opium. "No morbid appearance (says Mr. Whateley, the surgeon who opened the body) was found in any part of the body, except that the villous coat of the stomach was very slightly inflamed." The stimulus of the opium in this case either produced an action which transcended inflammation, or destroyed action altogether by its immense force, by which means the more common morbid appearances which follow disease in a dead body could not take place.

[81] Medical Transactions, vol. ii. p. 192.

[82] Ditto, p. 222.

[83] Bibliotheque Choisie de Medecine, tome xv. p. 212.

[84] Medical Essays of Edinburgh, vol. i. p. 226.

[85] Medical Commentaries, vol. iii. p. 496.

[86] Volume V.

[87] The hoarse barking, or the total inability of mad dogs to bark, favours still further the idea that the mortal seat of the disease is in the glottis, and that the remedy which has been proposed is a rational one.

AN ACCOUNT
OF
THE MEASLES,
AS THEY
APPEARED IN PHILADELPHIA,
IN THE SPRING OF 1789.

The weather in December, 1788, and in January, 1789, was variable, but seldom very cold. On the first of February, 1789, at six o'clock in the morning, the mercury in Fahrenheit's thermometer fell 5° below 0, in the city of Philadelphia. At twenty miles from the city, on the Schuylkill, it fell 12° below 0, at the same hour. On the 19th and 20th of this month, there fell a quantity of snow, the depth of which, upon an average, was supposed to be about eight or ten inches. On the 23d, 24th, 25th, and 27th, the weather was very cold. The mercury fluctuated during these days between 4° and 10° above 0.

In the intervals between these cold days, the weather frequently moderated, so that the Delaware was frozen and thawed not less than four times. It was not navigable till the 8th of March. There were in all, during the winter and month of March, sixteen distinct falls of snow.

In April and May there were a few warm days, but upon the whole, it was a very cold and backward spring. The peaches failed almost universally. There were no strawberries or cherries on the 24th of May, and every other vegetable product was equally backward. A country woman of 84 years of age informed me, that it was the coldest spring she had ever known. It was uncomfortable to sit without fire till the first of June.

The measles appeared first in the Northern Liberties, in December. They spread slowly in January, and were not universal in the city till February and March.

This disease, like many others, had its *precursor*. It was either a gum-boil, or a sore on the tongue. They were both very common, but not universal. They occurred, in some instances, several days before the fever, but in general they made their appearance during the eruptive fever, and were a sure mark of the approaching eruption of the measles. I was first led to observe this fact, from having read Dr. Quin's accurate account of the measles in Jamaica. I shall now proceed to mention the symptoms of the measles as they appeared in the different parts of the body.

1. In the *head*, they produced great pain, swelling of the eye-lids, so as to obstruct the eye-sight, tooth-ach, bleeding at the nose, tinnitus aurium, and deafness; also coma for two days, and convulsions. I saw the last symptom only in one instance. It was brought on by a stoppage of a running from the ear.

2. In the *throat* and *lungs*, they produced a soreness and hoarseness, acute or dull pains in the breast and sides, and a painful or distressing cough. In one case, this cough continued for two hours without any intermission, attended by copious expectoration. In two cases, I saw a constant involuntary discharge of phlegm and mucus from the mouth, without any cough. One of them terminated fatally. Spitting of blood occurred in several instances. The symptoms of pneumonia vera notha and typhoides were very common. I saw two fatal cases from pneumonia notha, in both of which the patients died with the trunk of the body in an erect posture. I met with two cases in which there was no cough till the eruption made its appearance on the fourth day, and one which was accompanied by all the usual symptoms of the cynanche trachealis.

3. In the *stomach* the measles produced, in many instances, sickness and vomiting. And

4. In the *bowels*, griping, diarrhœa, and, in some instances, bloody stools. The diarrhœa occurred in every stage of the disease, but it was bloody and most painful in its decline. I attended a black girl who discharged a great many worms, but without the least relief of any of her symptoms.

There was a great variety in this disease. 1. In the *time* of the attack of the fever, from the *time* of the reception of the contagion. In general the interval was fourteen days, but it frequently appeared before, and sometimes later than that period.

2. In the *time of the eruption*, from the beginning of the fever. It generally appeared on the third and fourth days. In one case, Dr. Waters informed me, it did not appear till the eighth day.

3. In the *abatement* or *continuance* of the fever after the eruption.

4. In the *colour* and *figure* of the eruption. In some it put on a *pale* red, in others a *deep*, and in a few a *livid* colour, resembling an incipient mortification. In some there appeared red blotches, in others an equally diffused redness, and in a few, eruptions like the small-pox, called by Dr. Cullen, rubiola varioloides.

5. In the *duration* of the eruption on the skin. It remained in most cases only three or four days; but in one, which came under my care, it remained nine days.

6. In the *manner of its retrocession.* I saw very few cases of its leaving the branny appearance so generally spoken of by authors on the skin.

7. In *not affecting* many persons, and even families who were exposed to it.

The symptoms which continued in many after the retrocession of the measles, were cough, hoarseness, or complete aphonia, which continued in two cases for two weeks; also diarrhœa, opthalmy, a bad taste in the mouth, a defect or excess of appetite, and a fever, which in some instances was of the intermitting kind, but which in more assumed the more dangerous form of the typhus mitior. Two cases of internal dropsy of the brain followed them. One was evidently excited by a fall. They both ended fatally.

During the prevalence of the disease I observed several persons (who had had the measles, and who were closely confined to the rooms of persons ill with them) to be affected with a slight cough, sore throat, and even sores in the mouth. I find a similar fact taken notice of by Dr. Quier.

But I observed further, many children to be affected by a fever, cough, and all the other symptoms of the measles which have been mentioned, except a general eruption, for in some there was a trifling efflorescence about the neck and breast. I observed the same thing in 1773 and 1783. In my note book I find the following account of the appearance of this disease in children in the year 1773. "The measles appeared in March; a catarrh (for by that name I then called it) appeared at the same time, and was often mistaken for them, the symptoms being nearly the same in both. In the catarrh there was in some instances a trifling eruption. A lax often attended it, and some who had it had an extremely sore mouth."

I was the more struck with this disease, from finding it was taken notice of by Dr. Sydenham. He calls it a morbillous fever. I likewise find an account of it in the 2d article of the 5th volume of the Edinburgh Medical Essays. The words of the author, who is anonymous, are as follow. "During this measly season, several persons, who never had the measles, had all the symptoms of measles, which went off in a few days without any eruptions. The same persons had the measles months or years afterwards." Is this disease a common fever, marked by the reigning epidemic, and produced in the same manner, and by the same causes, as the variolous fever described by Dr. Sydenham, which he says prevailed at the same time with the small-pox? I think it is not. My reasons for this opinion are as follow.

1. I never saw it affect any but children, in the degree that has been mentioned, and such only as had never had the measles.

2. It affected whole families at the same time. It proved fatal to one of three children whom it affected on the same day.

3. It terminated in a pulmonary consumption in a boy of ten years old, with all the symptoms which attend that disease when it follows the regular measles.

4. It affected a child in one family, on the same day that two other members of the same family were affected by the genuine measles.

5. It appeared on the usual days of the genuine measles, from the time the persons affected by it were exposed to its contagion. And,

6. It communicated the disease in one family, in the usual time in which the disease is taken from the genuine measles.

The measles, then, appear to follow the analogy of the small-pox, which affects so superficially as to be taken a second time, and which produce on persons who have had them what are called the nurse pock. They follow likewise the analogy of another disease, viz. the scarlatina anginosa. In the account of the epidemic for 1773, published in the third volume of the Edinburgh Medical Essays, we are told, that such patients as had previously had the scarlet fever without sore throats, took the sore throat, and had no eruption, while those who had previously had the sore throat had a scarlet eruption, but the throat remained free from the distemper. All other persons who were affected had both.

From these facts, I have taken the liberty of calling it the *internal measles*, to distinguish it from those which are *external*. I think the discovery of this new state of this disease of some application to practice.

1. It will lead us to be cautious in declaring any disease to be the external measles, in which there is not a general eruption. From my ignorance of this, I have been led to commit several mistakes, which were dishonourable to the profession. I was called, during the prevalence of the measles in the above-named season, to visit a girl of twelve years old, with an eruption on the skin. I called it the measles. The mother told me it was impossible, for that I had in 1783 attended her for the same disease. I suspect the anonymous author before-mentioned has fallen into the same error. He adds to the account before quoted the following words. "Others, who had undergone the measles formerly, had *at this time* a fever of the erysipelatous kind, with eruptions like to which nettles cause, and all the *previous* and concomitant symptoms of the measles, from the beginning to the end of the disease."

2. If inoculation, or any other mode of lessening the violence of the disease, should be adopted, it will be of consequence to know what persons are secure from the attacks of it, and who are still exposed to it.

I shall now add a short account of my method of treating this disease.

Many hundred families came through the disease without the help of a physician. But in many cases it was attended with peculiar danger, and in some with death. I think it was much more fatal than in the years 1773 and 1783, probably owing to the variable weather in the winter, and the coldness and dampness of the succeeding spring. Dr. Huxham says, he once saw the measles attended with peculiar mortality, during a late cold and damp spring in England. It was much more fatal (cæteris paribus) to adults than to young people.

The remedies I used were,

1. *Bleeding*, in all cases where great pain and cough with a hard pulse attended. In some I found it necessary to repeat this remedy. But I met with many cases in which it was forbidden by the weakness of the pulse, and by other marks of a feeble action in the blood-vessels.

2. *Vomits*. These were very useful in removing a nausea; they likewise favoured the eruption of the measles.

3. *Demulcent* and *diluting drinks*. These were barley water, bran, and flaxseed tea, dried cherry and raw apple water, also beverage, and cyder and water. The last drink I found to be the most agreeable to my patients of any that have been mentioned.

4. *Blisters* to the neck, sides, and extremities, according to the symptoms. They were useful in every stage of the disease.

5. *Opiates*. These were given not only at night, but in small doses during the day, when a troublesome cough or diarrhœa attended.

6. Where a catarrhal fever ensued, I used bleeding and blisters. In those cases in which this fever terminated in an intermittent, or in a mild typhus fever, I gave the bark with evident advantage. In that case of measles, formerly mentioned, which was accompanied by symptoms of cynanche trachealis, I gave calomel with the happiest effects. In the admission of *fresh air* I observed a medium as to its temperature, and accommodated it to the degrees of action in the system. In different parts of the country, in Pennsylvania and New-Jersey, I heard with great pleasure of the *cold air* being used as freely and as successfully in this disease, as in the inflammatory small-pox. The same people who were so much benefited by *cool air*, I was informed, drank plentifully of cold water during every stage of the fever. One thing in favour of this country practice deserves to be mentioned, and that is, evident advantage arose in all the cases which I attended, from patients leaving their beds in the febrile state of this disease. But this was practised

only by those in whom inflammatory diathesis prevailed, for these alone had strength enough to bear it.

The convalescent state of this disease required particular attention.

1. *A diarrhœa* often continued to be troublesome after other symptoms had abated. I relieved it by opiates and demulcent drinks. Bleeding has been recommended for it, but I did not find it necessary in a single case.

2. An *opthalmia* which sometimes attended, yielded to astringent collyria and blisters.

3. Where a cough or fever followed so slight as not to require bleeding, I advised a milk and vegetable diet, country air, and moderate warmth; for whatever might have been the relation of the lungs in the beginning of the disease to cold air, they were now evidently too much debilitated to bear it.

4. It is a common practice to prescribe purges after the measles. After the asthenic state of this disease they certainly do harm. In all cases, the effects of them may be better obviated by diet, full or low, suitable clothing, and gentle exercise, or country air. I omitted them in several cases, and no eruption or disease of any kind followed their disuse.

I shall only add to this account of the measles, that in several families, I saw evident advantages from preparing the body for the reception of the contagion, by means of a vegetable diet.

AN ACCOUNT
OF
THE INFLUENZA,
AS IT APPEARED
IN PHILADELPHIA,
IN THE AUTUMN OF 1789, IN THE SPRING OF
1790, AND IN THE WINTER OF 1791.

The latter end of the month of August, in the summer of 1789, was so very cool that fires became agreeable. The month of September was cool, dry, and pleasant. During the whole of this month, and for some days before it began, and after it ended, there had been no rain. In the beginning of October, a number of the members of the first congress, that had assembled in New-York, under the present national government, arrived in Philadelphia, much indisposed with colds. They ascribed them to the fatigue and night air to which they had been exposed in travelling in the public stages; but from the number of persons who were affected, from the uniformity of their complaints, and from the rapidity with which it spread through our city, it soon became evident that it was the disease so well known of late years by the name of the influenza.

The symptoms which ushered in the disease were generally a hoarseness, a sore throat, a sense of weariness, chills, and a fever. After the disease was formed, it affected more or less the following parts of the body. Many complained of acute pains in the *head.* These pains were frequently fixed between the eye-balls, and, in three cases which came under my notice, they were terminated by abscesses in the frontal sinus, which discharged themselves through the nose. The pain, in one of these cases, before the rupture of the abscess, was so exquisite, that my patient informed me, that he felt as if he should lose his reason. Many complained of a great itching in the *eye-lids.* In some, the eye-lids were swelled. In others, a copious effusion of water took place from the *eyes;* and in a few, there was a true ophthalmia. Many complained of great pains in one *ear,* and some of pains in both *ears.* In some, these pains terminated in abscesses, which discharged for some days a bloody or purulent matter. In others, there was a swelling behind each ear, without a suppuration.—*Sneezing* was a universal symptom. In some, it occurred not less than fifty times in a day. The matter discharged from the nose was so acrid as to inflame the nostrils and the upper lip, in such a manner as to bring on swellings, sores, and scabs in many people. In some, the nose discharged drops, and in a few, streams of blood, to the amount, in one case, of twenty ounces. In many cases, it was so much obstructed, as to render breathing through it difficult. In some, there was a total defect of *taste*. In others, there was a bad taste in the mouth, which frequently continued through the whole course of the disease. In some, there was a want of *appetite*. In others, it was perfectly natural. Some complained of a soreness in their mouths, as if they had been inflamed by holding pepper in them. Some had *swelled jaws*, and many complained of the *tooth-ach*. I saw only one case in which the disease produced a *coma*.

Many were affected with pains in the *breast* and *sides*. A difficulty of breathing attended in some, and a *cough* was universal. Sometimes this cough alternated with a pain in the *head*. Sometimes it preceded this pain, and sometimes it followed it. It was at all times distressing. In some instances, it resembled the chin-cough. One person expired in a fit of coughing, and many persons spat blood in consequence of its violence. I saw several patients in whom the disease affected the trachea chiefly, producing great difficulty of breathing, and, in one case, a suppression of the voice, and I heard of another in which the disease, by falling on the trachea, produced a cynanche trachealis. In most of the cases which terminated fatally, the patients died of pneumonia notha.

The *stomach* was sometimes affected by nausea and vomiting; but this was far from being a universal symptom.

I met with four cases in which the whole force of the disease fell upon the *bowels*, and went off in a diarrhœa; but in general the bowels were regular or costive.

The *limbs* were affected with such acute pains as to be mistaken for the rheumatism, or for the break-bone-fever of 1780. The pains were most acute in the back and thighs.

Profuse sweats appeared in many over the whole body in the beginning, but without affording any relief. It was in some instances accompanied by erysipelatous, and in four cases which came to my knowledge, it was followed by miliary eruptions.

The *pulse* was sometimes tense and quick, but seldom full. In a great majority of those whom I visited it was quick, weak, and soft.

There was no appearance in the urine different from what is common in all fevers.

The disease had evident remissions, and the fever seldom continued above three or four days; but the cough, and some other troublesome symptoms, sometimes continued two or three weeks.

In a few persons, the fever terminated in a tedious and dangerous typhus.

In several pregnant women it produced uterine hæmorrhages and abortions.

It affected adults of both sexes alike. A few old people escaped it. It passed by children under eight years old with a few exceptions. Out of five and thirty maniacs in the Pennsylvania hospital, but three were affected by it. No profession or occupation escaped it. The smell of tar and tobacco did not preserve the persons who worked in them from the disease, nor did the use of tobacco, in snuff, smoking, or chewing, afford a security against it.[88]

Even previous and existing diseases did not protect patients from it. It insinuated into sick chambers, and blended itself with every species of chronic complaint.

It was remarkable that persons who worked in the open air, such as sailors, and 'long-shore-men, (to use a mercantile epithet) had it much worse than tradesmen who worked within doors. A body of surveyors, in the eastern woods of Pennsylvania, suffered extremely from it. Even the vigour of constitution which is imparted by the savage life did not mitigate its violence. Mr. Andrew Ellicott, the geographer of the United States, informed me that he was a witness of its affecting the Indians in the neighbourhood of Niagara with peculiar force. The cough which attended this disease was so new and so irritating a complaint among them, that they ascribed it to witchcraft.

It proved most fatal on the sea-shore of the United States.

Many people who had recovered, were affected a second time with all the symptoms of the disease. I met with a woman, who, after recovering from it in Philadelphia, took it a second time in New-York, and a third time upon her return to Philadelphia.

Many thousand people had the disease who were not confined to their houses, but transacted business as usual out of doors. A perpetual coughing was heard in every street of the city. Buying and selling were rendered tedious by the coughing of the farmer and the citizen who met in market places. It even rendered divine service scarcely intelligible in the churches.

A few persons who were exposed to the disease escaped it, and some had it so lightly as scarcely to be sensible of it. Of the persons who were confined to their houses, not a fourth part of them kept their beds.

It proved fatal (with few exceptions) only to old people, and to persons who had been previously debilitated by consumptive complaints. It likewise carried of several hard drinkers. It terminated in asthma in three persons whose cases came under my notice, and in pulmonary consumption, in many more. I met with an instance in a lady, who was much relieved of a chronic complaint in her liver; and I heard of another instance of a clergyman whose general health was much improved by a severe attack of this disease.

It was not wholly confined to the human species. It affected two cats, two house-dogs, and one horse, within the sphere of my observations. One of the dogs disturbed his mistress so much by coughing at night, that she gave him ten drops of laudanum for several nights, which perfectly composed him. One of the cats had a vomiting with her cough. The horse breathed as if he had been affected by the cynanche trachealis.

The scarlatina anginosa, which prevailed during the summer, disappeared after the first of October; but appeared again after the influenza left the city. Nor was the remitting fever seen during the prevalence of the reigning epidemic.

I inoculated about twenty children for the small-pox during this prevalence of the influenza, and never saw that disease exhibit a more favourable appearance.

In the treatment of the influenza I was governed by the state of the system. Where inflammatory diathesis discovered itself by a full or tense pulse, or where great difficulty of breathing occurred, and the pulse was low and weak in the beginning of the disease, I ordered moderate bleeding. In a few cases in which the symptoms of pneumony attended, I bled a second time with advantage. In all these instances of inflammatory affection, I gave the usual antiphlogistic medicines. I found that vomits did not terminate the disease, as they often do a common catarrh, in the course of a day, or of a few hours.

In cases where no inflammatory action appeared in the system, I prescribed cordial drinks and diet, and forbad every kind of evacuation. I saw several instances of persons who had languished for a week or two with the disease, who were suddenly cured by eating a hearty meal, or by drinking half a pint of wine, or a pint of warm punch. In all these cases of weak action in the blood-vessels, liquid laudanum gave great relief, not only by suspending the cough, but by easing the pains in the bones.

I met with a case of an old lady who was suddenly and perfectly cured of her cough by a fright.

The duration of this epidemic in our city was about six weeks. It spread from New-York and Philadelphia in all directions, and in the course of a few months pervaded every state in the union. It was carried from the United

States to several of the West-India islands. It prevailed in the island of Grenada in the month of November, 1789, and it was heard of in the course of the ensuing winter in the Spanish settlements in South-America.

The following winter was unusually mild, insomuch that the navigation of the Delaware was not interrupted during the whole season, only from the 7th to the 24th of February. The weather on the 3d and 4th days of March was very cold, and on the 8th and 9th days of the same month, the mercury in Fahrenheit's thermometer stood at 4° at 7 o'clock in the morning. On the 10th and 11th, there fell a deep snow. The weather during the remaining part of the month was cold, rainy, and variable. It continued to be variable during the month of April. About the middle of the month there fell an unusual quantity of rain. The showers which fell on the night of the 17th will long be connected in the memories of the citizens of Philadelphia with the time of the death of the celebrated Dr. Franklin. Several pleurisies appeared during this month; also a few cases of measles. In the last week of the month the influenza made its appearance. It was brought to the city from New-England, and affected, in its course, all the intermediate states. Its symptoms were nearly the same as they were in the preceding autumn, but in many people it put on some new appearances. Several persons who were affected by it had symptoms of madness, one of whom destroyed himself by jumping out of a window. Some had no cough, but very acute pains in the back and head. It was remarked that those who had the disease chiefly in the breast the last year, complained now chiefly of their heads, while those whose heads were affected formerly, now complained chiefly of their breasts. In many it put on the type of an intermitting fever. Several complained of constant chills, or constant sweats; and some were much alarmed by an uncommon blue and dark colour in their hands. I saw one case of ischuria, another of an acute pain in the rectum, a third of anasarca, and a fourth of a palsy in the tongue and arms; all of which appeared to be anomalous symptoms of the influenza. Sneezing, and pains in the ears and frontal sinus, were less common now than they were in the fall; but a pain in the eye-balls was a universal symptom. Some had a pain in the one eye only, and a few had sore eyes, and swellings in the face. Many women who had it, were affected by an irregular appearance of the catamenia. In two persons whom I saw, the cough was incessant for three days, nor could it be composed by any other remedy than plentiful bleeding. A patient of Dr. Samuel Duffield informed me, after his recovery, that he had had no other symptom of the disease than an efflorescence on his skin, and a large swelling in his groin, which terminated in a tedious abscess.

The prisoners in the jail who had it in the autumn, escaped it this spring.

During the prevalence of this disease, I saw no sign of any other epidemic.

It declined sensibly about the first week in June, and after the 12th day of this month I was not called to a single patient in it.

The remedies for it were the same as were used in the fall.

I used bleeding in several cases on the second, third, and fourth days of the disease, where it had appeared to be improper in its first stage. The cases which required bleeding were far from being general. I saw two instances of syncope of an alarming nature, after the loss of ten ounces of blood; and I heard of one instance of a boy who died in half an hour after this evacuation.

I remarked that purges of all kinds worked more violently than usual in this disease.

The convalescence from it was very slow, and a general languor appeared to pervade the citizens for several weeks after it left the city.

The month of December, 1790, was extremely and uniformly cold. In the beginning of the month of January, 1791, the weather moderated, and continued to be pleasant till the 17th, on which day the navigation of the Delaware, which had been completely obstructed by the ice, was opened so as to admit of the arrival of several vessels. During the month of December many people complained of *colds*; but they were ascribed wholly to the weather. In January four or five persons in a family were affected by colds at the same time; which created a suspicion of a return of the influenza. This suspicion was soon confirmed by accounts of its prevailing in the neighbouring counties of Chester and Montgomery, in Pennsylvania, and in the distant states of Virginia and Rhode-Island. It did not affect near so generally as in the two former times of appearance. There was no difference in the method of treating it. While the common inflammatory diseases of the winter bore the lancet as usual, it was remarked that patients who were attacked by the influenza, did not bear bleeding in a greater proportion, or in a larger quantity, than in the two former times of its appearance in the city.

I shall conclude this account of the influenza by the following observations:

1. It exists independently of the sensible qualities of the air, and in all kinds of weather. Dr. Patrick Russel has proved the plague to be equally independent of the influence of the sensible qualities of the atmosphere, to a certain degree.

2. The influenza passes with the utmost rapidity through a country, and affects the greatest number of people, in a given time, of any disease in the world.

3. It appears from the histories of it which are upon record, that neither climate, nor the different states of society, have produced any *material* change in the disease. This will appear from comparing the account I have given, with the histories of it which have lately been given by Dr. Grey, Dr. Hamilton, Dr. A. Fothergill, Mr. Chisholm, and other modern physicians. It appears further, that even time itself has not been able materially to change the type of this disease. This is evident, from comparing modern accounts of it with those which have been handed down to us by ancient physicians.

I have hinted in a former essay at the *diminutives* of certain diseases. There is a state of influenza, which is less violent and more local, than that which has been described. It generally prevails in the winter season. It seems to originate from a morbid matter, generated in crowded and heated churches, and other assemblies of the people. I have seen a cold, or influenza, frequently universal in Philadelphia, which I have distinctly traced to this source. It would seem as if the same species of diseases resembled pictures, and that while some of them partook of the deep and vivid nature of mosaic work, others appeared like the feeble and transient impressions of water colours.

Footnote:

[88] Mr. Howard informs us that the use of tobacco is not a preservative against the plague, as has formerly been supposed; of course that apology for the use of an offensive weed should not be admitted.

AN INQUIRY
INTO THE
CAUSE OF ANIMAL LIFE.
IN THREE LECTURES,
DELIVERED IN THE UNIVERSITY OF
PENNSYLVANIA.

LECTURE I.

GENTLEMEN,

My business in this chair is to teach the institutes of medicine. They have been divided into physiology, pathology, and therapeutics. The objects of the first are, the laws of the human body in its healthy state. The second includes the history of the causes and seats of diseases. The subjects of the third are the remedies for those diseases. In entering upon the first part of our course, I am met by a remark delivered by Dr. Hunter in his introductory lectures to his course of anatomy. "In our branch (says the doctor) those teachers who study to captivate young minds with ingenious speculations, will not leave a reputation behind them that will outlive them half a century. When they cease from their labours, their labours will be buried along with them. There never was a man more followed and admired in physiology, than Dr. Boerhaave. I remember the veneration in which he was held. And now, in the space of forty years, his physiology is——it shocks me to think in what a light it appears[89]." Painful as this premonition may be to the teachers of physiology, it should not deter them from speculating upon physiological subjects. Simple anatomy is a mass of dead matter. It is physiology which infuses life into it. A knowledge of the structure of the human body occupies only the memory. Physiology introduces it to the higher and more noble faculties of the mind. The component parts of the body may be compared to the materials of a house, lying without order in a yard. It is physiology, like a skilful architect, which connects them together, so as to form from them an elegant and useful building. The writers against physiology resemble, in one particular, the writers against luxury. They forget that the functions they know and describe belong to the science of physiology; just as the declaimers against luxury forget that all the conveniences which they enjoy beyond what are possessed in the most simple stage of society, belong to the luxuries of life. The anatomist who describes the circulation of the blood, acts the part of a physiologist, as much as he does, who attempts to explain the functions of the brain. In this respect Dr. Hunter did honour to our science; for few men ever explained that subject, and many others equally physiological, with more perspicuity and eloquence, than that illustrious anatomist. Upon all new and difficult subjects there must be pioneers. It has been my lot to be called to this office of hazard and drudgery; and if in discharging its duties I should meet the fate of my predecessors, in this branch of medicine, I shall not perish in vain. My errors, like the bodies of those who fall in forcing a breach, will serve to compose a bridge for those who shall come after me, in our present difficult enterprise. This consideration, aided by just views of the nature and extent of moral obligation, will overbalance the evils anticipated by Dr. Hunter, from the loss of posthumous fame. Had a prophetic voice whispered in the ear of Dr. Boerhaave in the evening of his life, that in the short period of forty years, the memory of his physiological works would perish from the earth, I am satisfied, from the knowledge we have of his elevated genius and piety, he would have treated the prediction with the same indifference that he would have done, had he been told, that in the same time, his name should be erased from a pane of glass, in a noisy and vulgar country tavern.

The subjects of the lectures I am about to deliver, you will find in a syllabus which I have prepared and published, for the purpose of giving you a succinct view of the extent and connection of our course. Some of these subjects will be new in lectures upon the institutes of medicine, particularly those which relate to morals, metaphysics, and theology. However thorny these questions may appear, we must approach and handle them; for they are intimately connected with the history of the faculties and operations of the human mind; and these form an essential part of the animal economy. Perhaps it is because physicians have hitherto been restrained from investigating, and deciding upon these subjects, by an erroneous belief that they belong exclusively to another profession, that physiology has so long been an obscure and conjectural science.

In beholding the human body, the first thing that strikes us, is its *life*. This, of course, should be the first object of our inquiries. It is a most important subject; for the end of all the studies of a physician is to preserve life; and this cannot be perfectly done, until we know in what it consists.

I include in animal life, as applied to the human body, *motion, sensation,* and *thought.* These three, when united, compose perfect life. It may exist without thought, or sensation; but neither sensation, nor thought, can exist without motion. The lowest grade of life, probably exists in the absence of even motion, as I shall mention hereafter. I have preferred the term *motion* to those of oscillation and vibration, which have been employed by Dr. Hartley in explaining the laws of animal matter; because I conceived it to be more simple, and better adapted to common apprehension.

In treating upon this subject, I shall first consider animal life as it appears in the waking and sleeping states in a healthy adult, and shall afterwards inquire into the modification of its causes in the fœtal, infant, youthful, and middle states of life, in certain diseases, in different states of society, in different climates, and in different animals.

I shall begin by delivering three general propositions.

I. Every part of the human body (the nails and hair excepted) is endowed with sensibility, or excitability, or with both of them. By sensibility is meant the power of having sensation excited by the action of impressions. Excitability denotes that property in the human body, by which motion is excited by means of impressions. This property has been called by several other names, such as irritability, contractility, mobility, and stimulability.

I shall make use of the term excitability, for the most part, in preference to any of them. I mean by it, a capacity of imperceptible, as well as obvious motion. It is of no consequence to our present inquiries, whether this excitability be a quality of animal matter, or a substance. The latter opinion has been maintained by Dr. Girtanner, and has some probability in its favour.

II. The whole human body is so formed and connected, that impressions made in the healthy state upon one part, excite motion, or sensation, or both, in every other part of the body. From this view, it appears to be a unit, or a simple and indivisible quality, or substance. Its capacity for receiving motion, and sensation, is variously modified by means of what are called the senses. It is external, and internal. The impressions which act upon it shall be ennumerated in order.

III. Life is the *effect* of certain stimuli acting upon the sensibility and excitability which are extended, in different degrees, over every external and internal part of the body. These stimuli are as necessary to its existence, as air is to flame. Animal life is truly (to use the words of Dr. Brown) "a forced state." I have said the *words* of Dr. Brown; for the opinion was delivered by Dr. Cullen in the university of Edinburgh, in the year 1766, and was detailed by me in this school, many years before the name of Dr. Brown was known as teacher of medicine. It is true, Dr. Cullen afterwards deserted it; but it is equally true, I never did; and the belief of it has been the foundation of many of the principles and modes of practice in medicine which I have since adopted. In a lecture which I delivered in the year 1771, I find the following words, which are taken from a manuscript copy of lectures given by Dr. Cullen upon the institutes of medicine. "The human body is not an automaton, or self-moving machine; but is kept alive and in motion, by the constant action of stimuli upon it." In thus ascribing the discovery of the cause of life which I shall endeavour to establish, to Dr. Cullen, let it not be supposed I mean to detract from the genius and merit of Dr. Brown. To his intrepidity in reviving and propagating it, as well as for the many other truths contained in his system of medicine, posterity, I have no doubt, will do him ample justice, after the errors that are blended with them have been corrected, by their unsuccessful application to the cure of diseases.

Agreeably to our last proposition, I proceed to remark, that the action of the brain, the diastole and systole of the heart, the pulsation of the arteries, the contraction of the muscles, the peristaltic motion of the bowels, the absorbing power of the lymphatics, secretion, excretion, hearing, seeing, smelling, taste, and the sense of touch, nay more, thought itself, are all the effects of stimuli acting upon the organs of sense and motion. These stimuli have been divided into external and internal. The external are light, sound, odours, air, heat, exercise, and the pleasures of the senses. The internal stimuli are food, drinks, chyle, the blood, a certain tension of the glands, which contain secreted liquors, and the exercises of the faculties of the mind; each of which I shall treat in the order in which they have been mentioned.

1. Of external stimuli. The first of these is light. It is remarkable that the progenitor of the human race was not brought into existence until all the luminaries of heaven were created. Light acts chiefly through the medium of the organs of vision. Its influence upon animal life is feeble, compared with some other stimuli to be mentioned hereafter; but it has its proportion of force. Sleep has been said to be a tendency to death; now the absence of light we know invites to sleep, and the return of it excites the waking state. The late Mr. Rittenhouse informed me, that for many years he had constantly awoke with the first dawn of the morning light, both in summer and winter. Its influence upon the animal spirits strongly demonstrates its connection with animal life, and hence we find a cheerful and a depressed state of mind in many people, and more especially in invalids, to be intimately connected with the presence or absence of the rays of the sun. The well-known pedestrian traveller, Mr. Stewart, in one of his visits to this city, informed me, that he had spent a summer in Lapland, in the latitude of 69°, during the greatest part of which time the sun was seldom out of sight. He enjoyed, he said, during this period, uncommon health and spirits, both of which he ascribed to the long duration, and invigorating influence of light. These facts will surprise us less when we attend to the effects of light upon vegetables. Some of them lose their colour by being deprived of it; many of them discover a partiality to it in the direction of their flowers; and all of them discharge their pure air only while they are exposed to it[90].

2. Sound has an extensive influence upon human life. Its numerous artificial and natural sources need not be mentioned. I shall only take notice, that the currents of winds, the passage of insects through the air, and even

the growth of vegetables, are all attended with an emission of sound; and although they become imperceptible from habit, yet there is reason to believe they all act upon the body, through the medium of the ears. The existence of these sounds is established by the reports of persons who have ascended two or three miles from the earth in a balloon. They tell us that the silence which prevails in those regions of the air is so new and complete, as to produce an awful solemnity in their minds. It is not necessary that these sounds should excite sensation or perception, in order to their exerting a degree of stimulus upon the body. There are a hundred impressions daily made upon it, which from habit are not followed by sensation. The stimulus of aliment upon the stomach, and of blood upon the heart and arteries, probably cease to be felt, only from the influence of habit. The exercise of walking, which was originally the result of a deliberate act of the will, is performed from habit without the least degree of consciousness. It is unfortunate for this, and many other parts of physiology, that we forget what passed in our minds the first two or three years of our lives. Could we recollect the manner in which we acquired our first ideas, and the progress of our knowledge with the evolution of our senses and faculties, it would relieve us from many difficulties and controversies upon this subject. Perhaps this forgetfulness by children, of the origin and progress of their knowledge, might be remedied by our attending more closely to the first effects of impressions, sensation, and perception upon them, as discovered by their little actions; all of which probably have a meaning, as determined as any of the actions of men or women.

The influence of sounds of a certain kind in producing excitement, and thereby increasing life, cannot be denied. Fear produces debility, which is a tendency to death. Sound obviates this debility, and thus restores the system to the natural and healthy grade of life. The school-boy and the clown invigorate their feeble and trembling limbs by whistling or singing as they pass by a country church-yard, and the soldier feels his departing life recalled in the onset of a battle by the noise of the fife, and of the poet's "spirit stirring drum." Intoxication is frequently attended with a higher degree of life than is natural. Now sound we know will produce this with a very moderate portion of fermented liquor; hence we find men are more easily and highly excited by it at public entertainments where there is music, loud talking, and hallooing, than in private companies where there is no auxiliary stimulus added to that of the wine. I wish these effects of sound upon animal life to be remembered; for I shall mention it hereafter as a remedy for the weak state of life in many diseases, and shall relate an instance in which a scream suddenly extorted by grief, proved the means of resuscitating a person who was supposed to be dead, and who had exhibited the usual recent marks of the extinction of life.

I shall conclude this head by remarking, that persons who are destitute of hearing and seeing possess life in a more languid state than other people; and hence arise the dulness and want of spirits which they discover in their intercourse with the world.

3. Odours have a sensible effect in promoting animal life. The greater healthiness of the country, than cities, is derived in part from the effluvia of odoriferous plants, which float in the atmosphere in the spring and summer months, acting upon the system, through the medium of the sense of smelling. The effects of odours upon animal life appear still more obvious in the sudden revival of it, which they produce in cases of fainting. Here the smell of a few drops of hartshorn, or even of a burnt feather, has frequently in a few minutes restored the system, from a state of weakness bordering upon death, to an equable and regular degree of excitement.

4. Air acts as a powerful stimulus upon the system, through the medium of the lungs. The component parts of this fluid, and its decomposition in the lungs, will be considered in another place[91]. I shall only remark here, that the circulation of the blood has been ascribed, by Dr. Goodwin, exclusively to the action of air upon the lungs and heart. Does the external air act upon any other part of the body besides those which have been mentioned? It is probable it does, and that we lose our sensation and consciousness of it by habit. It is certain children cry, for the most part, as soon as they come into the world. May not this be the effect of the sudden impression of air upon the tender surface of their bodies? And may not the red colour of their skins be occasioned by an irritation excited on them by the stimulus of the air? It is certain it acts powerfully upon denudated animal fibres; for who has not observed a sore, and even the skin when deprived of its cuticle, to be affected, when long exposed to the air, with pain and inflammation? The stimulus of air, in promoting the natural actions of the alimentary canal, cannot be doubted. A certain portion of it seems to be necessarily present in the bowels in a healthy state.

5. Heat is a uniform and active stimulus in promoting life. It is derived, in certain seasons and countries, in part from the sun; but its principal source is from the lungs, in which it appears to be generated by the decomposition of pure air, and from whence it is conveyed, by means of the circulation, to every part of the body. The extensive influence of heat upon animal life, is evident from its decay and suspension during the winter in certain animals, and from its revival upon the approach and action of the vernal sun. It is true, life is diminished much less in man, from the distance and absence of the sun, than in other animals; but this must be ascribed to his possessing reason in so high a degree, as to enable him to supply the abstraction of heat, by the action of other stimuli upon his system.

6. Exercise acts as a stimulus upon the body in various ways. Its first impression is upon the muscles. These act upon the blood-vessels, and they upon the nerves and brain. The necessity of exercise to animal life is indicated, by its being kindly imposed upon man in paradise. The change which the human body underwent by the fall, rendered the same salutary stimulus necessary to its life, in the more active form of labour. But we are not to suppose, that motion is excited in the body by exercise or labour alone. It is constantly stimulated by the positions of standing, sitting, and lying upon the sides; all of which act more or less upon muscular fibres, and by their means, upon every part of the system.

7. The pleasures we derive from our senses have a powerful and extensive influence upon human life. The number of these pleasures, and their proximate cause, will form an agreeable subject for two or three future lectures.

We proceed next to consider the internal stimuli which produce animal life. These are

I. FOOD. This acts in the following ways. 1. Upon the tongue. Such are the sensibility and excitability of this organ, and so intimate is its connection with every other part of the body, that the whole system is invigorated by aliment, as soon as it comes in contact with it. 2. By mastication. This moves a number of muscles and blood-vessels situated near the brain and heart, and of course imparts impressions to them. 3. By deglutition, which acts upon similar parts, and with the same effect. 4. By its presence in the stomach, in which it acts by its quantity and quality. Food, by distending the stomach, stimulates the contiguous parts of the body. A moderate degree of distention of the stomach and bowels is essential to a healthy excitement of the system. Vegetable aliment and drinks, which contain less nourishment than animal food, serve this purpose in the human body. Hay acts in the same manner in a horse. Sixteen pounds of this light food in a day are necessary to keep up such a degree of distension in the stomach and bowels of this animal, as to impart to him his natural grade of strength and life. The *quality* of food, when of a stimulating nature, supplies the place of its distension from its quantity. A single onion will support a lounging highlander on the hills of Scotland for four and twenty hours. A moderate quantity of salted meat, or a few ounces of sugar, have supplied the place of pounds of less stimulating food. Even indigestible substances, which remain for days, or perhaps weeks in the stomach, exert a stimulus there which has an influence upon animal life. It is in this way the tops of briars, and the twigs of trees, devoid not only of nourishing matter, but of juices, support the camel in his journies through the deserts of the eastern countries. Chips of cedar posts moistened with water have supported horses for two or three weeks, during a long voyage from Boston to Surinam; and the indigestible cover of an old Bible preserved the life of a dog, accidentally confined in a room at Newcastle upon Tyne, for twenty days. 5. Food stimulates the whole body by means of the process of digestion which goes forward in the stomach. This animal function is carried on by a process, in which there is probably an extrication of heat and air. Now both these, it has been remarked, exert a stimulus in promoting animal life.

Drinks, when they consist of fermented or distilled liquors, stimulate from their quality; but when they consist of water, either in its simple state, or impregnated with any sapid substance, they act principally by distention.

II. The chyle acts upon the lacteals, mesenteric glands, and thoracic duct, in its passage through them; and it is highly probable, its first mixture with the blood in the subclavian vein, and its first action on the heart, are attended with considerable stimulating effects.

III. The blood is a very important internal stimulus. It has been disputed whether it acts by its quality, or only by distending the blood-vessels. It appears to act in both ways. I believe with Dr. Whytt, that the blood stimulates the heart and arteries by a specific action. But if this be not admitted, its influence in extending the blood-vessels in every part of the body, and thereby imparting extensive and uniform impressions to every animal fibre, cannot be denied. In support of this assertion it has been remarked, that in those persons who die of hunger, there is no diminution of the quantity of blood in the large blood-vessels.

IV. A certain *tension* of the glands, and of other parts of the body, contributes to support animal life. This is evident in the vigour which is imparted to the system, by the fulness of the seminal vesicles and gall bladder, and by the distension of the uterus in pregnancy. This distension is so great, in some instances, as to prevent sleep for many days and even weeks before delivery. It serves the valuable purpose of rendering the female system less liable to death during its continuance, than at any other time. By increasing the quantity of life in the body, it often suspends the fatal issue of pulmonary consumption, and ensures a temporary victory over the plague and other malignant fevers; for death, from those diseases, seldom takes place, until the stimulus, from the distension of the uterus, is removed by parturition.

V. The exercises of the faculties of the mind have a wonderful influence in increasing the quantity of human life. They all act by *reflection* only, after having been previously excited into action by impressions made upon the body. This view of the *re-action* of the mind upon the body accords with the simplicity of other operations in the animal economy. It is thus the brain repays the heart for the blood it conveys to it, by re-acting upon its muscular fibres. The influence of the different faculties of the mind is felt in the pulse, in the stomach, and in the liver, and is seen in the face, and other external parts of the body. Those which act most unequivocally in promoting life are the understanding, the imagination, and the passions. Thinking belongs to the understanding, and is attended with an obvious influence upon the degree and duration of life. Intense study has often rendered the body insensible to the debilitating effects of cold and hunger. Men of great and active understandings, who blend with their studies temperance and exercise, are generally long lived. In support of this assertion, a hundred names might be added to those of Newton and Franklin. Its truth will be more fully established by attending to the state of human life in persons of an opposite intellectual character. The cretins, a race of idiots in Valais, in Switzerland, travellers tell us, are all short lived. Common language justifies the opinion of the stimulus of the understanding upon the brain: hence it is common to say of dull men, that they have scarcely ideas enough to keep themselves awake.

The imagination acts with great force upon the body, whether its numerous associations produce pleasure or pain. But the passions pour a constant stream upon the wheels of life. They have been subdivided into emotions and passions properly so called. The former have for their objects present, the latter, future good and evil. All the objects of the passions are accompanied with desire or aversion. To the former belong chiefly, hope, love, ambition, and avarice; to the latter, fear, hatred, malice, envy, and the like. Joy, anger, and terror, belong to the class of emotions. The passions and emotions have been further divided into stimulating and sedative. Our business at present is to consider their first effect only upon the body. In the original constitution of human nature, we were made to be stimulated by such passions and emotions only as have moral good for their objects. Man was designed to be always under the influence of hope, love, and joy. By the loss of his innocence, he has subjected himself to the dominion of passions and emotions of a malignant nature; but they possess, in common with such as are good, a stimulus which renders them subservient to the purpose of promoting animal life. It is true, they are like the stimulus of a dislocated bone in their operation upon the body, compared with the action of antagonist muscles stretched over bones, which gently move in their natural sockets. The effects of the good passions and emotions, in promoting health and longevity, have been taken notice of by many writers. They produce a flame, gentle and pleasant, like oil perfumed with frankincense in the lamp of life. There are instances likewise of persons who have derived strength and long life from the influence of the evil passions and emotions that have been mentioned. Dr. Darwin relates the history of a man, who used to overcome the fatigue induced by travelling, by thinking of a person whom he hated. The debility induced by disease is often removed by a sudden change in the temper. This is so common, that even nurses predict a recovery in persons as soon as they become peevish and ill-natured, after having been patient during the worst stage of their sickness. This peevishness acts as a gentle stimulus upon the system in its languid state, and thus turns the scale in favour of life and health. The famous Benjamin Lay, of this state, who lived to be eighty years of age, was of a very irascible temper. Old Elwes was a prodigy of avarice, and every court in Europe furnishes instances of men who have attained to extreme old age, who have lived constantly under the dominion of ambition. In the course of a long inquiry which I instituted some years ago into the state of the body and mind in old people, I did not find a single person above eighty, who had not possessed an active understanding, or active passions. Those different and opposite faculties of the mind, when in excess, happily supply the place of each other. Where they unite their forces, they extinguish the flame of life, before the oil which feeds it is consumed.

In another place I shall resume the influence of the faculties of the mind upon human life, as they discover themselves in the different pursuits of men.

I have only to add here, that I see no occasion to admit, with the followers of Dr. Brown, that the mind is active in sleep, in preserving the motions of life. I hope to establish hereafter the opinion of Mr. Locke, that the mind is always passive in sound sleep. It is true it acts in dreams; but these depend upon a morbid state of the brain, and therefore do not belong to the present stage of our subject, for I am now considering animal life only in the healthy state of the body. I shall say presently, that dreams are intended to supply the absence of some natural stimulus, and hence we find they occur in those persons most commonly, in whom there is a want of healthy action in the system, induced by the excess or deficiency of customary stimuli.

Life is in a languid state in the morning. It acquires vigour by the gradual and successive application of stimuli in the forenoon. It is in its most perfect state about mid-day, and remains stationary for some hours. From the diminution of the sensibility and contractility of the system to the action of impressions, it lessens in the evening, and becomes again languid at bed-time. These facts will admit of an extensive application hereafter in our lectures upon the practice of physic.

LECTURE II.

GENTLEMEN,

The stimuli which have been enumerated, when they act collectively, and within certain bounds, produce a healthy waking state. But they do not always act collectively, nor in the determined and regular manner that has been described. There is, in many states of the system, a deficiency of some stimuli, and, in some of its states, an apparent absence of them all. To account for the continuance of animal life under such circumstances, two things must be premised, before we proceed to take notice of the diminution or absence of the stimuli which support it.

1. The healthy actions of the body in the waking state consist in a proper degree of what has been called excitability and excitement. The former is the medium on which stimuli act in producing the latter. In an exact proportion, and a due relation of both, diffused uniformly throughout every part of the body, consists good health. Disease is the reverse of this. It depends *in part* upon a disproportion between excitement and excitability, and in a partial distribution of each of them. In thus distinguishing the different states of excitement and excitability in health and sickness, you see I dissent from Dr. Brown, who supposes them to be (though disproportioned to each other) equably diffused in the morbid, as well as the healthy state of the body.

2. It is a law of the system, that the absence of one natural stimulus is generally supplied by the increased action of others. This is more certainly the case where a natural stimulus is abstracted *suddenly*; for the excitability is thereby so instantly formed and accumulated, as to furnish a highly sensible and moveable surface for the remaining stimuli to act upon. Many proofs might be adduced in support of this proposition. The reduction of the excitement of the blood-vessels, by means of cold, prepares the way for a full meal, or a warm bed, to excite in them the morbid actions which take place in a pleurisy or a rheumatism. A horse in a cold stable eats more than in a warm one, and thus counteracts the debility which would otherwise be induced upon his system, by the abstraction of the stimulus of warm air.

These two propositions being admitted, I proceed next to inquire into the different degrees and states of animal life. The first departure from its ordinary and perfect state which strikes us, is in

I. Sleep. This is either natural or artificial. Natural sleep is induced by a diminution of the excitement and excitability of the system, by the continued application of the stimuli which act upon the body in its waking state. When these stimuli act in a determined degree, that is, when the same number of stimuli act with the same force, and for the same time, upon the system, sleep will be brought on at the same hour every night. But when they act with uncommon force, or for an unusual time, it is brought on at an earlier hour. Thus a long walk or ride, by persons accustomed to a sedentary life, unusual exercise of the understanding, the action of strong passions or emotions, and the continual application of unusual sounds seldom fail of inducing premature sleep. It is recorded of pope Ganganelli, that he slept more soundly, and longer than usual, the night after he was raised to the papal chair. The effects of unusual sounds in bringing on premature sleep, is further demonstrated by that constant inclination to retire to bed at an early hour, which country people discover the first and second days they spend in a city, exposed from morning till night to the noise of hammers, files, and looms, or of drays, carts, waggons, and coaches, rattling over pavements of stone. Sleep is further hastened by the absence of light, the cessation of sounds and labour, and the recumbent posture of the body on a soft bed.

Artificial sleep may be induced at any time by certain stimulating substances, particularly by opium. They act by carrying the system beyond the healthy grade of excitement, to a degree of indirect debility, which Dr. Brown has happily called the sleeping point. The same point may be induced in the system at any time by the artificial abstraction of the usual stimuli of life. For example, let a person shut himself up at mid-day in a dark room, remote from noise of all kinds, let him lie down upon his back upon a soft bed in a temperate state of the atmosphere, and let him cease to think upon interesting subjects, or let him think only upon one subject, and he will soon fall asleep. Dr. Boerhaave relates an instance of a Dutch physician, who, having persuaded himself that waking was a violent state, and sleep the only natural one of the system, contrived, by abstracting every kind of stimulus in the manner that has been mentioned, to sleep away whole days and nights, until at length he impaired his understanding, and finally perished in a public hospital in a state of idiotism.

In thus anticipating a view of the cause of sleep, I have said nothing of the effects of diseases of the brain in inducing it. These belong to another part of our course. The short explanation I have given of its cause was necessary in order to render the history of animal life, in that state of the system, more intelligible.

At the usual hour of sleep there is an abstraction of the stimuli of light, sound, and muscular motion. The stimuli which remain, and act with an increased force upon the body in sleep, are

1. The heat which is discharged from the body, and confined by means of bed-clothes. It is most perceptible when exhaled from a bed-fellow. Heat obtained in this way has sometimes been employed to restore declining life to the bodies of old people. Witness the damsel who lay for this purpose in the bosom of the king of Israel. The advantage of this external heat will

appear further, when we consider how impracticable or imperfect sleep is, when we lie under too light covering in cold weather.

2. The air which is applied to the lungs during sleep probably acts with more force than in the waking state. I am disposed to believe that more air is phlogisticated in sleep than at any other time, for the smell of a close room in which a person has slept one night, we know, is much more disagreeable than that of a room, under equal circumstances, in which half a dozen people have sat for the same number of hours in the day time. The action of decomposed air on the lungs and heart was spoken of in a former lecture. An increase in its quantity must necessarily have a powerful influence upon animal life during the sleeping state.

3. Respiration is performed with a greater extension and contraction of the muscles of the breast in sleep than in the waking state; and this cannot fail of increasing the impetus of the blood in its passage through the heart and blood-vessels. The increase of the fulness and force of the pulse in sleep, is probably owing in part to the action of respiration upon it. In another place I hope to elevate the rank of the blood-vessels in the animal economy, by showing that they are the fountains of power in the body. They derive this pre-eminence from the protection and support they afford to every part of the system. They are the perpetual centineals of health and life; for they never partake in the repose which is enjoyed by the muscles and nerves. During sleep, their sensibility seems to be converted into contractility, by which means their muscular fibres are more easily moved by the blood than in the waking state. The diminution of sensibility in sleep is proved by many facts to be mentioned hereafter; and the change of sensibility into contractility will appear, when we come to consider the state of animal life in infancy and old age.

4. Aliment in the stomach acts more powerfully in sleep than in the waking state. This is evident from digestion going on more rapidly when we are awake than when we sleep. The more slow the digestion, the greater is the stimulus of the aliment in the stomach. Of this we have many proofs in daily life. Labourers object to milk as a breakfast, because it digests too soon; and often call for food in a morning, which they can feel all day in their stomachs. Sausages, fat pork, and onions are generally preferred by them for this purpose. A moderate supper is favourable to easy and sound sleep; and the want of it, in persons who are accustomed to that meal, is often followed by a restless night. The absence of its stimulus is probably supplied by a full gall-bladder (which always attends an empty stomach) in persons who are not in the habit of eating suppers.

5. The stimulus of the urine, accumulated in the bladder during sleep, has a perceptible influence upon animal life. It is often so considerable as to interrupt sleep; and it is one of the causes of our waking at a regular hour in the morning. It is moreover a frequent cause of the activity of the understanding and passions in dreams; and hence we dream more in our morning slumbers, when the bladder is full, than we do in the beginning or middle of the night.

6. The fæces exert a constant stimulus upon the bowels in sleep. This is so considerable as to render it less profound when they have been accumulated for two or three days, or when they have been deposited in the extremity of the alimentary canal.

7. The partial and irregular exercises of the understanding and passions in dreams have an occasional influence in promoting life. They occur only where there is a deficiency of other stimuli. Such is the force with which the mind acts upon the body in dreams, that Dr. Brambilla, physician to the emperor of Germany, informs us, that he has seen instances of wounds in soldiers being inflamed, and putting on a gangrenous appearance in consequence of the commotions excited in their bodies by irritating dreams[92]. The stimulating passions act through the medium of the will; and the exercises of this faculty of the mind sometimes extend so far as to produce actions in the muscles of the limbs, and occasionally in the whole body, as we see in persons who walk in their sleep. The stimulus of lust often awakens us with pleasure or pain, according as we are disposed to respect or disobey the precepts of our Maker. The angry and revengeful passions often deliver us, in like manner, from the imaginary guilt of murder. Even the debilitating passions of grief and fear produce an indirect operation upon the system that is favourable to life in sleep, for they excite that distressing disease called the night mare, which prompts us to speak, or halloo, and by thus invigorating respiration, overcomes the languid circulation of the blood in the heart and brain. Do not complain then, gentlemen, when you are bestrode by this midnight hag. She is kindly sent to prevent your sudden death. Persons who go to bed in good health, and are found dead the succeeding morning, are said most commonly to die of this disease.

I proceed now to inquire into the state of animal life in its different stages. I pass over for the present its history in generation. It will be sufficient only to remark in this place, that its first motion is produced by the stimulus of the male seed upon the female ovum. This opinion is not originally mine. You will find it in Dr. Haller[93]. The pungent taste which Mr. John Hunter discovered in the male seed renders it peculiarly fit for this purpose. No sooner is the female ovum thus set in motion, and the fœtus formed, than its capacity of life is supported,

1. By the stimulus of the heat which it derives from its connection with its mother in the womb.

2. By the stimulus of its own circulating blood.

3. By its constant motion in the womb after the third month of pregnancy. The absence of this motion for a few days is always a sign of the indisposition or death of a fœtus. Considering how early a child is accustomed to it, it is strange that a cradle should ever have been denied to it after it comes into the world.

II. In infants there is an absence of many of the stimuli which support life. Their excretions are in a great measure deficient in acrimony, and their mental faculties are too weak to exert much influence upon their bodies. But the absence of stimulus from those causes is amply supplied

1. By the very great excitability of their systems to those of light, sound, heat, and air. So powerfully do light and sound act upon them, that the Author of nature has kindly defended their eyes and ears from an excess of their impressions by imperfect vision and hearing, for several weeks after birth. The capacity of infants to be acted upon by moderate degrees of heat is evident from their suffering less from cold than grown people. This is so much the case, that we read, in Mr. Umfreville's account of Hudson's Bay, of a child that was found alive upon the back of its mother after she was frozen to death. I before hinted at the action of the air upon the bodies of new-born infants in producing the red colour of their skins. It is highly probable (from a fact formerly mentioned) that the first impression of the atmosphere which produces this redness is accompanied with pain, and this we know is a stimulus of a very active nature. By a kind law of sensation, impressions, that were originally painful, become pleasurable by repetition or duration. This is remarkably evident in the impression now under consideration, and hence we find infants at a certain age discover signs of an increase of life by their delightful gestures, when they are carried into the open air. Recollect further, gentlemen, what was said formerly of excitability predominating over sensibility in infants. We see it daily, not only in their patience of cold, but in the short time in which they cease to complain of the injuries they meet with from falls, cuts, and even severe surgical operations.

2. Animal life is supported in infants by their sucking, or feeding, nearly every hour in the day and night when they are awake. I explained formerly the manner in which food stimulated the system. The action of sucking supplies, by the muscles employed in it, the stimulus of mastication.

3. Laughing and crying, which are universal in infancy, have a considerable influence in promoting animal life, by their action upon respiration, and the circulation of the blood. Laughing exists under all circumstances,

independently of education or imitation. The child of the negro slave, born only to inherit the toils and misery of its parents, receives its master with a smile every time he enters his kitchen or a negro-quarter. But laughing exists in infancy under circumstances still more unfavourable to it; an instance of which is related by Mr. Bruce. After a journey of several hundred miles across the sands of Nubia, he came to a spring of water shaded by a few scrubby trees. Here he intended to have rested during the night, but he had not slept long before he was awakened by a noise which he perceived was made by a solitary Arab, equally fatigued and half famished with himself, who was preparing to murder and plunder him. Mr. Bruce rushed upon him, and made him his prisoner. The next morning he was joined by a half-starved female companion, with an infant of six months old in her arms. In passing by this child, Mr. Bruce says, it laughed and crowed in his face, and attempted to leap upon him. From this fact it would seem as if laughing was not only characteristic of our species, but that it was early and intimately connected with human life. The child of these Arabs had probably never seen a smile upon the faces of its ferocious parents, and perhaps had never (before the sight of Mr. Bruce) beheld any other human creature.

Crying has a considerable influence upon health and life in children. I have seen so many instances of its salutary effects, that I have satisfied myself it is as possible for a child to "cry and be fat," as it is to "laugh and be fat."

4. As children advance in life, the constancy of their appetites for food, and their disposition to laugh and cry, lessen, but the diminution of these stimuli is supplied by exercise. The limbs[94] and tongues of children are always in motion. They continue likewise to eat oftener than adults. A crust of bread is commonly the last thing they ask for at night, and the first thing they call for in the morning. It is now they begin to feel the energy of their mental faculties. This stimulus is assisted in its force by the disposition to prattle, which is so universal among children. This habit of converting their ideas into words as fast as they rise, follows them to their beds, where we often hear them talk themselves to sleep in a whisper, or to use less correct, but more striking terms, by *thinking aloud*.

5. Dreams act at an early period upon the bodies of children. Their smiles, startings, and occasional screams in their sleep appear to arise from them. After the third or fourth year of their lives, they sometimes confound them with things that are real. From observing the effects of this mistake upon the memory, a sensible woman whom I once knew, forbad her children to tell their dreams, lest they should contract habits of lying, by confounding imaginary with real events.

6. New objects, whether natural or artificial, are never seen by children without emotions of pleasure which act upon their capacity of life. The

effects of novelty upon the tender bodies of children may easily be conceived, by its friendly influence upon the health of invalids who visit foreign countries, and who pass months or years in a constant succession of new and agreeable impressions.

III. From the combination of all the stimuli that have been enumerated, human life is generally in excess from fifteen to thirty-five. It is during this period the passions blow a perpetual storm. The most predominating of them is the love of pleasure. No sooner does the system become insensible to this stimulus, than ambition succeeds it in,

IV. The middle stage of life. Here we behold man in his most perfect physical state. The stimuli which now act upon him are so far regulated by prudence, that they are seldom excessive in their force. The habits of order the system acquires in this period, continue to produce good health for many years afterwards; and hence bills of mortality prove that fewer persons die between forty and fifty-seven, than in any other seventeen years of human life.

V. In old age, the senses of seeing, hearing, and touch are impaired. The venereal appetite is weakened, or entirely extinguished. The pulse becomes slow, and subject to frequent intermissions, from a decay in the force of the blood-vessels. Exercise becomes impracticable, or irksome, and the operations of the understanding are performed with languor and difficulty. In this shattered and declining state of the system, the absence and diminution of all the stimuli which have been mentioned are supplied,

1. By an increase in the quantity, and by the peculiar quality of the food which is taken by old people. They generally eat twice as much as persons in middle life, and they bear with pain the usual intervals between meals. They moreover prefer that kind of food which is savoury and stimulating. The stomach of the celebrated Parr, who died in the one hundred and fiftieth year of his age, was found full of strong, nourishing aliment.

2. By the stimulus of the fæces, which are frequently retained for five or six days in the bowels of old people.

3. By the stimulus of fluids rendered preternaturally acrid by age. The urine, sweat, and even the tears of old people, possess a peculiar acrimony. Their blood likewise loses part of the mildness which is natural to that fluid; and hence the difficulty with which sores heal in old people; and hence too the reason why cancers are more common in the decline, than in any other period of human life.

4. By the uncommon activity of certain passions. These are either good or evil. To the former belong an increased vigour in the operations of those passions which have for their objects the Divine Being, or the whole family of mankind, or their own offspring, particularly their grand-children. To the latter passions belong malice, a hatred of the manners and fashions of the rising generation, and, above all, avarice. This passion knows no holidays. Its stimulus is constant, though varied daily by the numerous means which it has discovered of increasing, securing, and perpetuating property. It has been observed that weak mental impressions produce much greater effects in old people than in persons in middle life. A trifling indisposition in a grand-child, an inadvertent act of unkindness from a friend, or the fear of losing a few shillings, have, in many instances, produced in them a degree of wakefulness that has continued for two or three nights. It is to this highly excitable state of the system that Solomon probably alludes, when he describes the grasshopper as burdensome to old people.

5. By the passion for talking, which is so common, as to be one of the characteristics of old age. I mentioned formerly the influence of this stimulus upon animal life. Perhaps it is more necessary in the female constitution than in the male; for it has long ago been remarked, that women who are very taciturn, are generally unhealthy.

6. By their wearing warmer clothes, and preferring warmer rooms, than in the former periods of their lives. This practice is so uniform, that it would not be difficult, in many cases, to tell a man's age by his dress, or by finding out at what degree of heat he found himself comfortable in a close room.

7. By dreams. These are universal among old people. They arise from their short and imperfect sleep.

8. It has been often said, that "We are once men, and twice children." In speaking of the state of animal life in infancy, I remarked that the contractility of the animal fibres predominated over their sensibility in that stage of life. The same thing takes place in old people, and it is in consequence of the return of this infantile state of the system, that all the stimuli which have been mentioned act upon them with much more force than in middle life. This sameness, in the predominance of excitability over sensibility in children and old people, will account for the similarity of their habits with respect to eating, sleep, exercise, and the use of fermented and distilled liquors. It is from the increase of excitability in old people, that so small a quantity of strong drink intoxicates them; and it is from an ignorance of this change in their constitutions, that many of them become drunkards, after passing the early and middle stages of life with sober characters.

Life is continued in a less imperfect state in old age in women than in men. The former sew, and knit, and spin, after they lose the use of their ears and eyes; whereas the latter, after losing the use of those senses, frequently pass the evening of their lives in a torpid state in a chimney corner. It is from the influence of moderate and gently stimulating employments, upon the female constitution, that more women live to be old than men, and that they rarely survive their usefulness in domestic life.

Hitherto the principles I am endeavouring to establish have been applied to explain the cause of life in its more common forms. Let us next inquire, how far they will enable us to explain its continuance in certain morbid states of the body, in which there is a diminution of some, and an apparent abstraction of all the stimuli, which have been supposed to produce animal life.

I. We observe some people to be blind, or deaf and dumb from their birth. The same defects of sight, hearing, and speech, are sometimes brought on by diseases. Here animal life is deprived of all those numerous stimuli, which arise from light, colours, sounds, and speech. But the absence of these stimuli is supplied,

1. By increased sensibility and excitability in their remaining senses. The ears, the nose, and the fingers, afford a surface for impressions in blind people, which frequently overbalances the loss of their eye-sight. There are two blind young men, brothers, in this city, of the name of Dutton, who can tell when they approach a post in walking across a street, by a peculiar sound which the ground under their feet emits in the neighbourhood of the post. Their sense of hearing is still more exquisite to sounds of another kind. They can tell the names of a number of tame pigeons, with which they amuse themselves in a little garden, by only hearing them fly over their heads. The celebrated blind philosopher, Dr. Moyse, can distinguish a black dress on his friends, by its smell; and we read of many instances of blind persons who have been able to perceive colours by rubbing their fingers upon them. One of these persons, mentioned by Mr. Boyle, has left upon record an account of the specific quality of each colour as it affected his sense of touch. He says black imparted the most, and blue the least perceptible sense of asperity to his fingers.

2. By an increase of vigour in the exercises of the mental faculties. The poems of Homer, Milton, and Blacklock, and the attainments of Sanderson in mathematical knowledge, all discover how much the energy of the mind is increased by the absence of impressions upon the organs of vision.

II. We sometimes behold life in idiots, in whom there is not only an absence of the stimuli of the understanding and passions, but frequently, from the weakness of their bodies, a deficiency of the loco-motive powers.

Here an inordinate appetite for food, or venereal pleasures, or a constant habit of laughing, or talking, or playing with their hands and feet, supply the place of the stimulating operations of the mind, and of general bodily exercise. Of the inordinate force of the venereal appetite in idiots we have many proofs. The cretins are much addicted to venery; and Dr. Michaelis tells us that the idiot whom he saw at the Passaic falls in New-Jersey, who had passed six and twenty years in a cradle, acknowledged that he had venereal desires, and wished to be married, for, the doctor adds, he had a sense of religion upon his fragment of mind, and of course did not wish to gratify that appetite in an unlawful manner.

III. How is animal life supported in persons who pass many days, and even weeks without food, and in some instances without drinks? Long fasting is usually the effect of disease, of necessity, or of a principle of religion. When it arises from the first cause, the actions of life are kept up by the stimulus of disease[95]. The absence of food when accidental, or submitted to as a means of producing moral happiness, is supplied,

1. By the stimulus of a full gall bladder. This state of the receptacle of bile has generally been found to accompany an empty stomach. The bile is sometimes absorbed, and imparts a yellow colour to the skin of persons who suffer or die of famine.

2. By increased acrimony in all the secretions and excretions of the body. The saliva becomes so acrid by long fasting, as to excoriate the gums, and the breath acquires not only a fœtor, but a pungency so active, as to draw tears from the eyes of persons who are exposed to it.

3. By increased sensibility and excitability in the sense of touch. The blind man mentioned by Mr. Boyle, who could distinguish colours by his fingers, poooooooed this talent only after fasting. Even a draught of any kind of liquor deprived him of it. I have taken notice, in my account of the yellow fever in Philadelphia, in the year 1793, of the effects of a diet bordering upon fasting for six weeks, in producing a quickness and correctness in my perceptions of the state of the pulse, which I had never experienced before.

4. By an increase of activity in the understanding and passions. Gamesters often improve the exercises of their minds, when they are about to play for a large sum of money, by living for a day or two upon roasted apples and cold water. Where the passions are excited into preternatural action, the absence of the stimulus of food is scarcely felt. I shall hereafter mention the influence of the desire of life upon its preservation, under all circumstances. It acts with peculiar force when fasting is accidental. But when it is submitted to as a religious duty, it is accompanied by sentiments and feelings which

more than balance the abstraction of aliment. The body of Moses was sustained, probably without a miracle, during an abstinence of forty days and forty nights, by the pleasure he derived from conversing with his Maker "face to face, as a man speaking with his friend[96]."

I remarked formerly, that the veins discover no deficiency of blood in persons who die of famine. Death from this cause seems to be less the effect of the want of food, than of the combined and excessive operation of the stimuli, which supply its place in the system.

IV. We come now to a difficult inquiry, and that is, how is life supported during the total abstraction of external and internal stimuli which takes place in asphyxia, or in apparent death, from all its numerous causes?

I took notice, in a former lecture, that ordinary life consisted in the excitement and excitability of the different parts of the body, and that they were occasionally changed into each other. In apparent death from violent emotions of the mind, from the sudden impression of miasmata, or from drowning, there is a loss of excitement; but the excitability of the system remains for minutes, and, in some instances, for hours afterwards unimpaired, provided the accident which produced the loss of excitement has not been attended with such exertions as are calculated to waste it. If, for example, a person should fall suddenly into the water, without bruising his body, and sink before his fears or exertions had time to dissipate his excitability; his recovery from apparent death might be effected by the gentle action of heat or frictions upon his body, so as to convert his accumulated excitability gradually into excitement. The same condition of the system takes place when apparent death occurs from freezing, and a recovery is accomplished by the same gentle application of stimuli, provided the organization of the body be not injured, or its excitability wasted, by violent exertions previously to its freezing. This excitability is the vehicle of motion, and motion, when continued long enough, produces sensation, which is soon followed by thought; and in these, I said formerly, consists perfect life in the human body.

For this explanation of the manner in which life is suspended and revived, in persons apparently dead from cold, I am indebted to Mr. John Hunter, who supposes, if it were possible for the body to be *suddenly* frozen, by an instantaneous abstraction of its heat, life might be continued for many years in a suspended state, and revived at pleasure, provided the body were preserved constantly in a temperature barely sufficient to prevent re-animation, and never so great as to endanger the destruction of any organic part. The resuscitation of insects, that have been in a torpid state for months, and perhaps years, in substances that have preserved their organization, should at least defend this bold proposition from being treated as chimerical. The effusions even of the imagination of such men as Mr. Hunter, are entitled to respect. They often become the germs of future discoveries.

In that state of suspended animation which occurs in acute diseases, and which has sometimes been denominated a *trance*, the system is nearly in the same excitable state that it is in apparent death from drowning and freezing. Resuscitation, in these cases, is not the effect, as in those which have been mentioned, of artificial applications made to the body for that purpose. It appears to be spontaneous; but it is produced by impressions made upon the ears, and by the operations of the mind in dreams. Of the actions of these stimuli upon the body in its apparently lifeless state, I have satisfied myself by many facts. I once attended a citizen of Philadelphia, who died of a pulmonary disease, in the 80th year of his age. A few days before his death, he begged that he might not be interred until one week after the usual signs of life had left his body, and gave as a reason for this request, that he had, when a young man, died to all appearance of the yellow fever, in one of the West-India islands. In this situation he distinctly heard the persons who attended him, fix upon the time and place of burying him. The horror of being put under ground alive, produced such distressing emotions in his mind, as to diffuse motion throughout his body, and finally excited in him all the usual functions of life. In Dr. Creighton's essay upon mental derangement, there is a history of a case nearly of a similar nature. A young lady (says the doctor), an attendant on the princess of——, after having been confined to her bed for a great length of time, with a violent nervous disorder, was at last, to all appearance, deprived of life. Her lips were quite pale, her face resembled the countenance of a dead person, and her body grew cold. She was removed from the room in which *she died*, was laid in a coffin, and the day for her funeral was fixed on. The day arrived, and according to the custom of the country, funeral songs and hymns were sung before the door. Just as the people were about to nail on the lid of the coffin, a kind of perspiration was observed on the surface of her body. She recovered. The following is the account she gave of her sensations: she said, "It seemed to her as if in a dream, that she was really dead; yet she was perfectly conscious of all that happened around her. She distinctly heard her friends speaking and lamenting her death at the side of her coffin. She felt them pull on the dead clothes, and lay her in it. This feeling produced a mental anxiety which she could not describe. She tried to cry out, but her mind was without power, and could not act on her body. She had the contradictory feeling as if she were in her own body, and not in it, at the same time. It was equally impossible for her to stretch out her arm or open her eyes, as to cry, although she continually endeavoured to do so. The internal anguish of her mind was at its utmost height when the funeral hymns began to be sung, and when the lid of the coffin was about to be nailed on. The thought that she was to be buried alive was the first which gave activity to her mind, and enabled it to operate on her corporeal frame."

Where the ears lose their capacity of being acted upon by stimuli, the mind, by its operations in dreams, becomes a source of impressions which again sets the wheels of life in motion. There is an account published by Dr. Arnold, in his observations upon insanity[97], of a certain John Engelbreght, a German, who was believed to be dead, and who was evidently resuscitated by the exercises of his mind upon subjects which were of a delightful or stimulating nature. This history shall be taken from Mr. Engelbreght's words. "It was on Thursday noon (says he), about twelve o'clock, when I perceived that death was making his approaches upon me from the lower parts upwards, insomuch that my whole body became stiff. I had no feeling left in my hands and feet, neither in any other part of my whole body, nor was I at last able to speak or see, for my mouth now becoming very stiff, I was no longer able to open it, nor did I feel it any longer. My eyes also broke in my head in such a manner that I distinctly felt it. For all that, I understood what they said, when they were praying by me, and I distinctly heard them say, feel his legs, how stiff and cold they have become. This I heard distinctly, but I had no perception of their touch. I heard the watchman cry 11 o'clock, but at 12 o'clock my hearing left me." After relating his passage from the body to heaven with the velocity of an arrow shot from a cross bow, he proceeds, and says, that as he was twelve hours in dying, so he was twelve hours in returning to life. "As I died (says he) from beneath upwards, so I revived again the contrary way, from above to beneath, or from top to toe. Being conveyed back from the heavenly glory, I began to hear something of what they were praying for me, in the same room with me. Thus was my hearing the *first* sense I recovered. After this I began to have a perception of my eyes, so that, by little and little, my whole body became strong and sprightly, and no sooner did I get a feeling of my legs and feet, than I arose and stood firm upon them with a firmness I had never enjoyed before. The heavenly joy I had experienced, invigorated me to such a degree, that people were astonished at my rapid, and almost instantaneous recovery."

The explanation I have given of the cause of resuscitation in this man will serve to refute a belief in a supposed migration of the soul from the body, in cases of apparent death. The imagination, it is true, usually conducts the whole mind to the abodes of happy or miserable spirits, but it acts here in the same way that it does when it transports it, in common dreams, to numerous and distant parts of the world.

There is nothing supernatural in Mr. Engelbreght being invigorated by his supposed flight to heaven. Pleasant dreams always stimulate and strengthen the body, while dreams which are accompanied with distress or labour debilitate and fatigue it.

LECTURE III.

GENTLEMEN,

Let us next take a view of the state of animal life in the different inhabitants of our globe, as varied by the circumstances of civilization, diet, situation, and climate.

I. In the Indians of the northern latitudes of America there is often a defect of the stimulus of aliment, and of the understanding and passions. Their vacant countenances, and their long and disgusting taciturnity, are the effects of the want of action in their brains from a deficiency of ideas; and their tranquillity under all the common circumstances of irritation, pleasure, or grief, are the result of an absence of passion; for they hold it to be disgraceful to show any outward signs of anger, joy, or even of domestic affection. This account of the Indian character, I know, is contrary to that which is given of it by Rousseau, and several other writers, who have attempted to prove that man may become perfect and happy without the aids of civilization and religion. This opinion is contradicted by the experience of all ages, and is rendered ridiculous by the facts which are well ascertained in the history of the customs and habits of our American savages. In a cold climate they are the most miserable beings upon the face of the earth. The greatest part of their time is spent in sleep, or under the alternate influence of hunger and gluttony. They moreover indulge in vices which are alike contrary to moral and physical happiness. It is in consequence of these habits that they discover so early the marks of old age, and that so few of them are long-lived. The absence and diminution of many of the stimuli of life in these people is supplied in part by the violent exertions with which they hunt and carry on war, and by the extravagant manner with which they afterwards celebrate their exploits, in their savage dances and songs.

II. In the inhabitants of the torrid regions of Africa there is a deficiency of labour; for the earth produces spontaneously nearly all the sustenance they require. Their understandings and passions are moreover in a torpid state. But the absence of bodily and mental stimuli in these people is amply supplied by the constant heat of the sun, by the profuse use of spices in their diet, and by the passion for musical sounds which so universally characterises the African nations.

III. In Greenland the body is exposed during a long winter to such a degree of cold as to reduce the pulse to 40 or 50 strokes in a minute. But the effects of this cold in lessening the quantity of life are obviated in part by the heat of close stove rooms, by warm clothing, and by the peculiar nature of the aliment of the Greenlanders, which consists chiefly of animal food, of dried fish, and of whale oil. They prefer the last of those articles in so rancid a state, that it imparts a fœtor to their perspiration, which, Mr. Crantz says, renders even their churches offensive to strangers. I need hardly add, that a diet possessed of such diffusible qualities cannot fail of being highly stimulating. It is remarkable that the food of all the northern nations of Europe is composed of stimulating animal or vegetable matters, and that the use of spiritous liquors is universal among them.

IV. Let us next turn our eyes to the miserable inhabitants of those eastern countries which compose the Turkish empire. Here we behold life in its most feeble state, not only from the absence of physical, but of other stimuli which operate upon the inhabitants of other parts of the world. Among the poor people of Turkey there is a general deficiency of aliment. Mr. Volney in his Travels tells us, "That the diet of the Bedouins seldom exceeds six ounces a day, and that it consists of six or seven dates soaked in butter-milk, and afterwards mixed with a little sweet milk, or curds." There is likewise a general deficiency among them of stimulus from the operations of the mental faculties; for such is the despotism of the government in Turkey, that it weakens not only the understanding, but it annihilates all that immense source of stimuli which arises from the exercise of the domestic and public affections. A Turk lives wholly to himself. In point of time he occupies only the moment in which he exists; for his futurity, as to life and property, belongs altogether to his master. Fear is the reigning principle of his actions, and hope and joy seldom add a single pulsation to his heart. Tyranny even imposes a restraint upon the stimulus which arises from conversation, for "They speak (says Mr. Volney) with a slow feeble voice, as if the lungs wanted strength to propel air enough through the glottis to form distinct articulate sounds." The same traveller adds, that "They are slow in all their motions, that their bodies are small, that they have small evacuations, and that their blood is so destitute of serosity, that nothing but the greatest heat can preserve its fluidity." The deficiency of aliment, and the absence of mental stimuli in these people is supplied,

1. By the heat of their climate.

2. By their passion for musical sounds and fine clothes. And

3. By their general use of coffee, garlic[98], and opium.

The more debilitated the body is, the more forcibly these stimuli act upon it. Hence, according to Mr. Volney, the Bedouins, whose slender diet has been mentioned, enjoy good health; for this consists not in strength, but in an exact proportion being kept up between the excitability of the body, and the number and force of the stimuli which act upon it.

V. Many of the observations which have been made upon the inhabitants of Africa, and of the Turkish dominions, apply to the inhabitants of China and the East-Indies. They want, in many instances, the stimulus of animal food. Their minds are, moreover, in a state too languid to act with much force upon their bodies. The absence and deficiency of these stimuli are supplied by,

1. The heat of the climate in the southern parts of those countries.

2. By a vegetable diet abounding in nourishment, particularly rice and beans.

3. By the use of tea in China, and by a stimulating coffee made of the dried and toasted seeds of the datura stramonium, in the neighbourhood of the Indian coast. Some of these nations likewise chew stimulating substances, as too many of our citizens do tobacco.

Among the poor and depressed subjects of the governments of the middle and southern parts of Europe, the deficiency of the stimulus of wholesome food, of clothing, of fuel, and of liberty, is supplied, in some countries, by the invigorating influence of the christian religion upon animal life, and in others by the general use of tea, coffee, garlic, onions, opium, tobacco, malt liquors, and ardent spirits. The use of each of these stimuli seems to be regulated by the circumstances of climate. In cold countries, where the earth yields its increase with reluctance, and where vegetable aliment is scarce, the want of the stimulus of distension which that species of food is principally calculated to produce is sought for in that of ardent spirits. To the southward of 40°, a substitute for the distension from mild vegetable food is sought for in onions, garlic, and tobacco. But further, a uniform climate calls for more of these artificial stimuli than a climate that is exposed to the alternate action of heat and cold, winds and calms, and of wet and dry weather. Savages and ignorant people likewise require more of them than persons of civilized manners, and cultivated understandings. It would seem from these facts that man cannot exist without *sensation* of some kind, and that when it is not derived from natural means, it will always be sought for in such as are artificial.

In no part of the human species, is animal life in a more perfect state than in the inhabitants of Great Britain[99], and the United States of America. With all the natural stimuli that have been mentioned, they are constantly under the invigorating influence of liberty. There is an indissoluble union between moral, political, and physical happiness; and if it be true, that elective and representative governments are most favourable to individual, as well as national prosperity, it follows of course, that they are most favourable to animal life. But this opinion does not rest upon an induction derived from the relation, which truths upon all subjects bear to each other. Many facts prove animal life to exist in a larger quantity and for a longer time, in the enlightened and happy state of Connecticut, in which republican liberty has existed above one hundred and fifty years, than in any other country upon the surface of the globe.

It remains now to mention certain mental stimuli which act nearly alike in the production of animal life, upon the individuals of all the nations in the world. They are,

1. The desire of life. This principle, so deeply and universally implanted in human nature, acts very powerfully in supporting our existence. It has been observed to prolong life. Sickly travellers by sea and land, often live under circumstances of the greatest weakness, till they reach their native country, and then expire in the bosom of their friends. This desire of life often turns the scale in favour of a recovery in acute diseases. Its influence will appear, from the difference in the periods in which death was induced in two persons, who were actuated by opposite passions with respect to life. Atticus, we are told, died of voluntary abstinence from food in five days. In sir William Hamilton's account of the earthquake at Calabria, we read of a girl who lived eleven days without food before she expired. In the former case, life was shortened by an aversion from it; in the latter, it was protracted by the desire of it. The late Mr. Brissot, in his visit to this city, informed me, that the application of animal magnetism (in which he was a believer) had in no instance cured a disease in a West-India slave. Perhaps it was rendered inert by its not being accompanied by a strong desire of life; for this principle exists in a more feeble state in slaves than in freemen. It is possible likewise the wills and imaginations of these degraded people may have become so paralytic by slavery, as to be incapable of being excited by the impression of this fanciful remedy.

2. The love of money sets the whole animal machine in motion. Hearts which are insensible to the stimuli of religion, patriotism, love, and even of the domestic affections, are excited into action by this passion. The city of Philadelphia, between the 10th and 15th of August, 1791, will long be remembered by contemplative men, for having furnished the most extraordinary proofs of the stimulus of the love of money upon the human body. A new scene of speculation was produced at that time by the scrip of the bank of the United States. It excited febrile diseases in three persons who

became my patients. In one of them, the acquisition of twelve thousand dollars in a few minutes by a lucky sale, brought on madness which terminated in death in a few days[100]. The whole city felt the impulse of this paroxysm of avarice. The slow and ordinary means of earning money were deserted, and men of every profession and trade were seen in all our streets hastening to the coffee-house, where the agitation of countenance, and the desultory manners, of all the persons who were interested in this species of gaming, exhibited a truer picture of a bedlam, than of a place appropriated to the transaction of mercantile business. But further, the love of money discovers its stimulus upon the body in a peculiar manner in the games of cards and dice. I have heard of a gentleman in Virginia who passed two whole days and nights in succession at a card table, and it is related in the life of a noted gamester in Ireland, that when he was so ill as to be unable to rise from his chair, he would suddenly revive when brought to the hazard table, by hearing the rattling of the dice.

3. Public amusements of all kinds, such as a horse race, a cockpit, a chase, the theatre, the circus, masquerades, public dinners, and tea parties, all exert an artificial stimulus upon the system, and thus supply the defect of the rational exercises of the mind.

4. The love of dress is not confined in its stimulating operation to persons in health. It acts perceptibly in some cases upon invalids. I have heard of a gentleman in South-Carolina, who always relieved himself of a fit of low spirits by changing his dress; and I believe there are few people who do not feel themselves enlivened, by putting on a new suit of clothes.

5. Novelty is an immense source of agreeable stimuli. Companions, studies, pleasures, modes of business, prospects, and situations, with respect to town and country, or to different countries, that are *new*, all exert an invigorating influence upon health and life.

6. The love of fame acts in various ways; but its stimulus is most sensible and durable in military life. It counteracts in many instances the debilitating effects of hunger, cold, and labour. It has sometimes done more, by removing the weakness which is connected with many diseases. In several instances it has assisted the hardships of a camp life, in curing pulmonary consumption.

7. The love of country is a deep seated principle of action in the human breast. Its stimulus is sometimes so excessive, as to induce disease in persons who recently migrate, and settle in foreign countries. It appears in various forms; but exists most frequently in the solicitude, labours, attachments, and hatred of party spirit. All these act forcibly in supporting animal life. It is

because newspapers are supposed to contain the measure of the happiness or misery of our country, that they are so interesting to all classes of people. Those vehicles of intelligence, and of public pleasure or pain, are frequently desired with the impatience of a meal, and they often produce the same stimulating effects upon the body[101].

8. The different religions of the world, by the activity they excite in the mind, have a sensible influence upon human life. Atheism is the worst of sedatives to the understanding and passions. It is the abstraction of thought from the most sublime, and of love from the most perfect of all possible objects. Man is as naturally a religious, as he is a social and domestic animal; and the same violence is done to his mental faculties, by robbing him of a belief in a God, that is done by dooming him to live in a cell, deprived of the objects and pleasures of social and domestic life. The necessary and immutable connection between the texture of the human mind, and the worship of an object of some kind, has lately been demonstrated by the atheists of Europe, who, after rejecting the true God, have instituted the worship of nature, of fortune, and of human reason; and, in some instances, with ceremonies of the most expensive and splendid kind. Religions are friendly to animal life, in proportion as they elevate the understanding, and act upon the passions of hope and love. It will readily occur to you, that christianity, when believed and obeyed, according to its original consistency with itself, and with the divine attributes, is more calculated to produce those effects than any other religion in the world. Such is the salutary operation of its doctrines and precepts upon health and life, that if its divine authority rested upon no other argument, this alone would be sufficient to recommend it to our belief. How long mankind may continue to prefer substituted pursuits and pleasures to this invigorating stimulus, is uncertain; but the time, we are assured, will come, when the understanding shall be elevated from its present inferior objects, and the luxated passions be reduced to their original order. This change in the mind of man, I believe, will be effected only by the influence of the christian religion, after all the efforts of human reason to produce it, by means of civilization, philosophy, liberty, and government, have been exhausted to no purpose.

Thus far, gentlemen, we have considered animal life as it respects the human species; but the principles I am endeavouring to establish require that we should take a view of it in animals of every species, in all of which we shall find it depends upon the same causes as in the human body.

And here I shall begin by remarking, that if we should discover the stimuli which support life in certain animals to be fewer in number, or weaker in force than those which support it in our species, we must resolve it into that attribute of the Deity which seems to have delighted in variety in all his works.

The following observations apply more or less to all the animals upon our globe.

1. They all possess either hearts, lungs, brains, nerves, or muscular fibres. It is as yet a controversy among naturalists whether animal life can exist without a brain; but no one has denied muscular fibres, and of course contractility, or excitability, to belong to animal life in all its shapes.

2. They all require more or less air for their existence. Even the snail inhales it for seven months under ground, through a pellicle which it weaves out of slime, as a covering for its body. If this pellicle at any time become too thick to admit the air, the snail opens a passage in it for that purpose. Now air we know acts powerfully in supporting animal life.

3. Many of them possess heat equal to that of the human body. Birds possess several degrees beyond it. Now heat, it was said formerly, acts with great force in the production of animal life.

4. They all feed upon substances more or less stimulating to their bodies. Even water itself, chemistry has taught us, affords an aliment, not only stimulating, but nourishing to many animals.

5. Many of them possess senses, more acute and excitable, than the same organs in the human species. These expose surfaces for the action of external impressions, that supply the absence or deficiency of mental faculties.

6. Such of them as are devoid of sensibility, possess an uncommon portion of contractility, or simple excitability. This is most evident in the polypus. When cut to pieces, it appears to feel little or no pain.

7. They all possess loco-motive powers in a greater or less degree, and of course are acted upon by the stimulus of muscular motion.

8. Most of them appear to feel a stimulus, from the gratification of their appetites for food, and for venereal pleasures, far more powerful than that which is felt by our species from the same causes. I shall hereafter mention some facts from Spalanzani upon the subject of generation, that will prove the stimulus, from venery, to be strongest in those animals, in which other stimuli act with the least force. Thus the male frog during its long connection with its female, suffers its limbs to be amputated, without discovering the least mark of pain, and without relaxing its hold of the object of its embraces.

9. In many animals we behold evident marks of understanding and passion. The elephant, the fox, and the ant exhibit strong proofs of thought;

and where is the school boy that cannot bear testimony to the anger of the bee and the wasp?

10. But what shall we say of those animals, which pass long winters in a state in which there is an apparent absence of the stimuli of heat, exercise, and the motion of the blood. Life in these animals is probably supported,

1. By such an accumulation of excitability, as to yield to impressions, which to us are imperceptible.

2. By the stimulus of aliment in a state of digestion in the stomach, or by the stimulus of aliment restrained from digestion by means of cold; for Mr. John Hunter has proved by an experiment on a frog, that cold below a certain degree, checks that animal process.

3. By the constant action of air upon their bodies.

It is possible life may exist in these animals, during their hybernation, in the total absence of impression and motion of every kind. This may be the case where the torpor from cold has been *suddenly* brought upon their bodies. Excitability here is in an accumulated, but quiescent state.

11. It remains only under this head to inquire, in what manner is life supported in those animals which live in a cold element, and whose blood is sometimes but a little above the freezing point? It will be a sufficient answer to this question to remark, that heat and cold are relative terms, and that different animals, according to their organization, require very different degrees of heat for their existence. Thirty-two degrees of it are probably as stimulating to some of these cold blooded animals (as they are called), as 70° or 80° are to the human body.

It might afford additional support to the doctrine of animal life, which I have delivered, to point out the manner in which life and growth are produced in vegetables of all kinds. But this subject belongs to the professor of botany and natural history[102], who is amply qualified to do it justice. I shall only remark, that vegetable life is as much the offspring of stimuli as animal, and that skill in agriculture consists chiefly in the proper application of them. The seed of a plant, like an animal body, has no principle of life within itself. If preserved for many years in a drawer, or in earth below the stimulating influence of heat, air, and water, it discovers no sign of vegetation. It grows, like an animal, only in consequence of stimuli acting upon its *capacity* of life.

From a review of what has been said of animal life in all its numerous forms and modifications, we see that it as much an effect of impressions upon a peculiar species of matter, as sound is of the stroke of a hammer upon a bell, or music of the motion of the bow upon the strings of a violin. I exclude therefore the intelligent principle of Whytt, the medical mind of Stahl, the healing powers of Cullen, and the vital principal of John Hunter, as much from the body, as I do an intelligent principle from air, fire, and water.

It is no uncommon thing for the simplicity of causes to be lost in the magnitude of their effects. By contemplating the wonderful functions of life we have strangely overlooked the numerous and obscure circumstances which produce it. Thus the humble but true origin of power in the people is often forgotten in the splendour and pride of governments. It is not necessary to be acquainted with the precise nature of that form of matter, which is capable of producing life from impressions made upon it. It is sufficient for our purpose to know the fact. It is immaterial, moreover, whether this matter derives its power of being acted upon wholly from the brain, or whether it be in part inherent in animal fibres. The inferences are the same in favour of life being the effect of stimuli, and of its being as truly mechanical as the movements of a clock from the pressure of its weights, or the passage of a ship in the water from the impulse of winds and tide.

The infinity of effects from similar causes, has often been taken notice of in the works of the Creator. It would seem as if they had all been made after one pattern. The late discovery of the cause of combustion has thrown great light upon our subject. Wood and coal are no longer believed to contain a principle of fire. The heat and flame they emit are derived from an agent altogether external to them. They are produced by a matter which is absorbed from the air, by means of its decomposition. This matter acts upon the predisposition of the fuel to receive it, in the same way that stimuli act upon the human body. The two agents differ only in their effects. The former produces the destruction of the bodies upon which it acts, while the latter excite the more gentle and durable motions of life. Common language in expressing these effects is correct, as far as it relates to their cause, We speak of a coal of fire being *alive*, and of the *flame* of life.

The causes of life which I have delivered will receive considerable support by contrasting them with the causes of death. This catastrophe of the body consists in such a change induced on it by disease or old age, as to prevent its exhibiting the phenomena of life. It is brought on,

1. By the abstraction of all the stimuli which support life. Death from this cause is produced by the same mechanical means that the emission of sound from a violin is prevented by the abstraction of the bow from its strings.

2. By the excessive force of stimuli of all kinds. No more occurs here than happens from too much pressure upon the strings of a violin preventing its emitting musical tones.

3. By too much relaxation, or too weak a texture of the matter which composes the human body. No more occurs here than is observed in the extinction of sound by the total relaxation, or slender combination of the strings of a violin.

4. By an error in the place of certain fluid or solid parts of the body. No more occurs here than would happen from fixing the strings of a violin upon its body, instead of elevating them upon its bridge.

5. By the action of poisonous exhalations, or of certain fluids vitiated in the body, upon parts which emit most forcibly the motions of life. No more happens here than occurs from enveloping the strings of a violin in a piece of wax.

6. By the solution of continuity by means of wounds in solid parts of the body. No more occurs in death from this cause than takes place when the emission of sound from a violin is prevented by a rupture of its strings.

7. Death is produced by a preternatural rigidity, and in some instances by an ossification of the solid parts of the body in old age, in consequence of which they are incapable of receiving and emitting the motions of life. No more occurs here, than would happen if a stick or pipe-stem were placed in the room of catgut, upon the bridges of the violin. But death may take place in old age without a change in the texture of animal matter, from the stimuli of life losing their effect by repetition, just as opium, from the same cause, ceases to produce its usual effects upon the body.

Should it be asked, what is that peculiar organization of matter, which enables it to emit life, when acted upon by stimuli, I answer, I do not know. The great Creator has kindly established a witness of his unsearchable wisdom in every part of his works, in order to prevent our forgetting him, in the successful exercises of our reason. Mohammed once said, "that he should believe himself to be a God, if he could bring down rain from the clouds, or give life to an animal." It belongs exclusively to the true God to endow matter with those singular properties, which enable it, under certain circumstances, to exhibit the appearances of life.

I cannot conclude this subject, without taking notice of its extensive application to medicine, metaphysics, theology, and morals.

The doctrine of animal life which has been taught, exhibits in the first place, a new view of the nervous system, by discovering its origin in the extremities of the nerves, on which impressions are made, and its termination in the brain. This idea is extended in an ingenious manner by Mr. Valli, in his treatise upon animal electricity.

2. It discovers to us the true means of promoting health and longevity, by proportioning the number and force of stimuli to the age, climate, situation, habits, and temperament of the human body.

3. It leads us to a knowledge of the causes of all diseases. These consist in excessive or preternatural excitement in the whole, or a part of the human body, accompanied *generally* with irregular motions, and induced by natural or artificial stimuli. The latter have been called, very properly, by Mr. Hunter, *irritants*. The occasional absence of motion in acute diseases is the effect only of the excess of impetus in their remote causes.

4. It discovers to us that the cure of all diseases depends simply upon the abstraction of stimuli from the whole, or from a part of the body, when the motions excited by them are in excess; and in the increase of their number and force, when motions are of a moderate nature. For the former purpose, we employ a class of medicines known by the name of sedatives. For the latter, we make use of stimulants. Under these two extensive heads, are included all the numerous articles of the materia medica.

5. It enables us to reject the doctrine of innate ideas, and to ascribe all our knowledge of sensible objects to impressions acting upon an *innate* capacity to receive ideas. Were it possible for a child to grow up to manhood without the use of any of its senses, it would not possess a single idea of a material object; and as all human knowledge is compounded of simple ideas, this person would be as destitute of knowledge of every kind, as the grossest portion of vegetable or fossil matter.

6. The account which has been given of animal life, furnishes a striking illustration of the origin of human actions, by the impression of motives upon the will. As well might we admit an inherent principle of life in animal matter, as a self-determining power in this faculty of the mind. Motives are necessary, not only to constitute its *freedom*, but its *essence*; for, without them, there could be no more a will, than there could be vision without light, or hearing without sound. It is true, they are often so obscure as not to be perceived, and they sometimes become insensible from habit; but the same things have been remarked in the operation of stimuli, and yet we do not upon this account deny their agency in producing animal life. In thus deciding in favour of the necessity of motives, to produce actions, I cannot help bearing a testimony against the gloomy misapplication of this doctrine by some modern writers. When properly understood, it is calculated to produce the most comfortable views of the divine government, and the most beneficial effects upon morals and human happiness.

7. There are errors of an impious nature, which sometimes obtain a currency, from being disguised by innocent names. The doctrine of animal life that has been delivered is directly opposed to an error of this kind, which

has had the most baneful influence upon morals and religion. To suppose a principle to reside necessarily and constantly in the human body, which acted independently of external circumstances, is to ascribe to it an attribute, which I shall not connect, even in language, with the creature man. Self-existence belongs only to God.

The best criterion of the truth of a philosophical opinion, is its tendency to produce exalted ideas of the Divine Being, and humble views of ourselves. The doctrine of animal life which has been delivered is calculated to produce these effects in an eminent degree, for

8. It does homage to the Supreme Being, as the governor of the universe, and establishes the certainty of his universal and particular providence. Admit a principle of life in the human body, and we open a door for the restoration of the old Epicurean or atheistical philosophy, which supposed the world to be governed by a principle called nature, and which was believed to be inherent in every kind of matter. The doctrine I have taught, cuts the sinews of this error; for by rendering the *continuance* of animal life, no less than its commencement, the effect of the constant operation of divine power and goodness, it leads us to believe that the whole creation is supported in the same manner.

9. The view that has been given of the dependent state of man for the blessing of life, leads us to contemplate, with very opposite and inexpressible feelings, the sublime idea which is given of the Deity in the scriptures, as possessing life "within himself." This divine prerogative has never been imparted but to one being, and that is the Son of God. This appears from the following declaration. "For as the Father hath life in himself, so hath he given to the Son to have life *within himself*."[103] To this plenitude of independent life, we are to ascribe his being called the "life of the world," "the prince of life," and "life" itself, in the New Testament. These divine epithets which are very properly founded upon the manner of our Saviour's existence, exalt him infinitely above simple humanity, and establish his divine nature upon the basis of reason, as well as revelation.

10. We have heard that some of the stimuli which produce animal life, are derived from the moral and physical evils of our world. From beholding these instruments of death thus converted by divine skill into the means of life, we are led to believe goodness to be the supreme attribute of the Deity, and that it will appear finally to predominate in all his works.

11. The doctrine which has been delivered, is calculated to humble the pride of man by teaching him his constant dependence upon his Maker for his existence, and that he has no pre-eminence in his tenure of it, over the meanest insect that flutters in the air, or the humblest plant that grows upon the earth. What an inspired writer says of the innumerable animals which

inhabit the ocean, may with equal propriety be said of the whole human race. "Thou sendest forth thy spirit, and they are created. Thou takest away their breath—they die, and return to their dust."

12. Melancholy indeed would have been the issue of all our inquiries, did we take a final leave of the human body in its state of decomposition in the grave. Revelation furnishes us with an elevating, and comfortable assurance that this will not be the case. The precise manner of its re-organization, and the new means of its future existence, are unknown to us. It is sufficient to believe, the event will take place, and that after it, the soul and body of man will be exalted in one respect, to an equality with their Creator. They will be immortal.

Here, gentlemen, we close the history of animal life. I feel as if I had waded across a rapid and dangerous stream. Whether I have gained the opposite shore with my head clean, or covered with mud and weeds, I leave wholly to your determination.

Footnotes:

[89] Lect. xi. p. 198.

[90] "Organization, sensation, spontaneous motion, and life, exist only at the surface of the earth, and in places exposed to *light*. We might affirm the flame of Prometheus's torch was the expression of a philosophical truth that did not escape the ancients. Without light, nature was lifeless, inanimate, and dead. A benevolent God, by producing life, has spread organization, sensation, and thought over the surface of the earth."—*Lavoisier.*

[91] It is probable, the first impulse of life was imparted to the body of Adam by the decomposition of air in his lungs. I infer this from the account given by Moses of his creation, in Genesis, chap. ii. v. 7. "And the Lord God formed man of the dust of the ground, and breathed into his nostrils the breath of life," in consequence of which, the verse adds, he became "a living soul." This explanation of the origin of life in the father of the human race, appears to accord more with reason, as well as the order of the words which describe it, than the common opinion of his having been animated by the infusion of a living soul into his body.

[92] A fever was excited in Cinna the poet, in consequence of his dreaming that he saw Cæsar, the night after he was assassinated, and was invited to accompany him to a dreary place, to which he pointed, in order to sup with him. Convulsions and other diseases, I believe, are often excited in the night, by terrifying or distressing dreams.

Plutarch's Life of M. Brutus.

[93] "Novum fœtum a seminis masculi *stimulo* vitam concepisse."—*Elementa Physiologiæ*, vol. viii. p. 177.

[94] Niebuhr, in his Travels, says the children in Arabia are taught to keep themselves constantly in motion by a kind of vibratory exercise of their bodies. This motion counteracts the diminution of life produced by the heat of the climate of Arabia.

[95] The stimulus of a disease sometimes supplies the place of food in prolonging life. Mr. C. S——, a gentleman well known in Virginia, who was afflicted with a palsy, which had resisted the skill of several physicians, determined to destroy himself, by abstaining from food and drinks. He lived *sixty* days without eating any thing, and the greatest part of that time without tasting even a drop of water. His disease probably protracted his life thus long beyond the usual time in which death is induced by fasting. See a particular account of this case, in the first number of the second volume of Dr. Coxe's Medical Museum.

[96] Exodus xxxiii, 11. xxxiv, 28.

[97] Vol. ii. p. 298.

[98] Niebuhr's Travels.

[99] Haller's Elements Physiologiæ, vol. viii. p. 2. p. 107.

[100] Dr. Mead relates, upon the authority of Dr. Hales, that more of the successful speculators in the South-Sea scheme of 1720 became insane, than of those who had been ruined by it.

[101] They have been very happily called by Mr. Green, in his poem entitled Spleen, "the manna of the day."

[102] Dr. Barton.

[103] John v. verse 26.

END OF VOL. II.

Booksophile
Your Local Online Bookstore

Buy Books Online from
www.Booksophile.com

Explore our collection of books written in various languages and uncommon topics from different parts of the world, including history, art and culture, poems, autobiography and bibliographies, cooking, action & adventure, world war, fiction, science, and law.

Add to your bookshelf or gift to another lover of books - first editions of some of the most celebrated books ever published. From classic literature to bestsellers, you will find many first editions that were presumed to be out-of-print.

Free shipping globally for orders worth US$ 100.00.

Use code "Shop_10" to avail additional 10% on first order.

Visit today
www.booksophile.com

Ingram Content Group UK Ltd.
Milton Keynes UK
UKHW011704130323
418485UK00004B/311

9 789356 895706